Folens
Science in Action

Year 3

Author Team:
Jo Powell
Simon Smith
Anne Whitehead
Steve Sizmur

© 2004 Folens Limited, on behalf of the authors.

Boscombe Road, Dunstable, LU5 4RL.
Email: folens@folens.com

Ireland: Folens Publishers, Greenhills Road, Tallaght, Dublin 24.
Email: info@folens.ie

Poland: JUKA, ul. Renesansowa 38, Warsaw 01-905.

Editor: Nancy Terry
Layout artist: Patricia Hollingsworth
Illustrations: Lee Sullivan
Cover design: Martin Cross

First published 2004 by Folens Limited.

British Library Cataloguing in Publication Data. A catalogue record for this publication is available from the British Library.

ISBN 1 84303 576 6

Contents

Introduction

Folens Science in Action is a complete course in upper primary (junior) science. It meets the requirements for the National Curriculum in England and Wales, and is compatible with the scheme of work published in England by the Qualifications and Curriculum Authority (QCA).

Aims of Folens Science in Action

The overall aim of the book is that children should come to understand, appreciate and respect the scientific approach to understanding the world, to recognise how science affects their lives and to have the enthusiasm to engage with scientific ideas for themselves.

Children should:
- cooperate to develop an understanding of themselves and of the world in which they live
- realise that scientific knowledge is built on reliable and agreed evidence
- know some of the scientific ways of talking about the world and related terminology
- use developing skills to subject their own and others' ideas to critical evaluation
- develop respect for their environment and the living things within it.

The Structure of Folens Science in Action and the Materials

Year 3 is divided into six units of work. The units are based on those in the scheme of work published by the QCA in England. Each unit is intended to occupy 10–12 hours of teaching time and is focused on a specific aspect of science. You can use the units in any order you prefer.
We recommend:

Autumn Term	Spring Term	Summer Term
Units C and E	Units A and D	Units B and F

One unit comprises up to five lessons. Most are intended to be taught in a single session. In specific cases, however, because investigations need to take place over an extended period, the lesson may need to be spread over more than one session.

The unit begins with an indication of the main scientific ideas covered in the unit. These ideas are covered at varying levels through the book as a whole. The time you will need to allocate to the unit is also shown.

For each lesson, a full lesson plan is provided, and the *Science Background* and *Learning Objectives* are made clear. The lessons begin with an *Introduction*, normally intended to be carried out with the whole class, which provides the context for the work of the lesson. This is followed by a *Main Activity*, usually requiring work in small groups. The whole-class *Plenary* is used to draw the work of the lesson together. This discussion is important for clarifying what has been learned, and you should ensure that enough time is allocated for this. During this time you can make judgements about whether the lesson objectives have been achieved and take the opportunity for corrective action, if necessary. Throughout, there are examples of questions to ask the children and of what the children will need to be told. You should adapt these to suit the children in your class.

The children's work is supported by photocopiable pupil sheets, which are fully referenced in the lesson plans.

Introduction

Progression and Differentiation

Folens Science in Action has been carefully constructed to ensure that scientific ideas are introduced and developed systematically over the course of the book. Key objectives are identified in each lesson by a ■. It is expected that the large majority of children will achieve these objectives. You should aim to provide additional support for children who struggle to reach these targets. For some lessons, pupil sheets are provided. For those who need further stretching, additional challenge is provided through the *Your Challenge ...* section of the pupil sheets. Resource sheets, marked by **RS**, are used to support the children's work both during the lesson and as they work on the pupil sheets.

Further differentiation is possible in the scientific enquiries that the children undertake. Different children can address the same investigative task with different amounts of direction and support, and they can take the investigation to different levels. The lessons are planned so that most children will make appropriate progress in enquiry skills. However, you should use your ongoing assessment to identify those children who need help as well as those who may be prompted to move on to a higher level of skill.

Assessment and Record-keeping

Progress in scientific enquiry can be assessed as opportunities arise in the course of investigative work using the *Assessment Grid: Scientific Enquiry* on the next page. The levels are equivalent to the National Curriculum levels used in England, Wales and Northern Ireland to measure the children's progress.

The *What to Look For* section in each lesson gives a more specific indication of the evidence you should look for in judging whether children have achieved the lesson objectives. At the end of the work on a particular unit, you should use the *Assessment Grid: Scientific Enquiry* provided to assess the level of the children's scientific knowledge and understanding. Use the grid to come to an overall judgement of the level reached by individual children, based on the set of descriptions that most closely match the child's performance overall.

You can obtain additional evidence by using the photocopiable test material at the end of each unit. Children should be able to work through the questions independently, but you should give them any help they need in reading them. Clarify what the questions are asking for as necessary, but do not explain the meaning of any scientific terms used. Children should have any language or other support normally available to them.

The unit *Assessment Grid*s give an indication of the range of marks you can expect children at the different levels to obtain. These marks should support, not replace, the evidence from your ongoing observational judgements.

The *Record Form* on page 78 can be used to keep a cumulative record of the children's attainment as they work through the book. On this form, the scientific stories have been grouped under the different areas of science.

Assessment Grid: Scientific Enquiry

Children working at level 1 typically:	Children working at level 2 typically:	Children working at level 3 typically:
Planning		
• Respond to objects and events.	• Respond to suggestions about how to find things out. • With help, raise their own questions and make their own suggestions about how to collect evidence to answer questions. • With help, say what they think will happen.	• Respond to suggestions, raise their own questions and put forward ideas about how to find out the anwer to a question. • Recognise why it is important to collect evidence to answer questions and test ideas. • With support, predict outcomes.
Obtaining and Presenting Evidence		
• Observe and describe objects and events.	• Use simple information sources and equipment provided. • Make relevant observations. • Compare objects, living things and events, noticing similarities and differences. • Use non-standard and simple standard measures. • Describe their observations using scientific vocabulary and record them in simple tables, block graphs and pictograms.	• Use information sources to locate information. • Make relevant observations. • Notice similarities and differences. • Make standard measurements of quantities such as mass and length. • Use a range of simple equipment and, with help, select appropriate familiar equipment. • With some help, make fair tests and explain why a comparison is/is not fair. • Record their observations using scientific vocabulary and in various ways including tables, bar charts and pictograms.
Considering Evidence and Evaluating		
• Communicate findings in simple terms.	• Say whether what happened was what they thought would happen. • With support, make comparisons and use results to draw conclusions.	• Explain observations and simple patterns in measurements. • Compare their evidence with their predictions. • Use scientific vocabulary to communicate what they have found out.

Unit A

Teeth and Eating

Scientific Enquiry: ● Scientists think creatively about how our world works and gather evidence to test their ideas using observation and measurement.
Life Processes and Living Things: ● Living things all carry out seven life processes. ● Humans (like other animals) have life processes which are maintained by organ systems.
Approximate Teaching Time: 12 hours

Assessment Grid

Unit 3A

	Below level 2, children typically:	At level 2, children typically:	At level 3, children typically:
Humans and Other Animals	● use descriptive words to talk about animals and plants. ● name familiar living things and distinguish them from non-living things.	● sort objects into groups according to specific criteria. ● know some of the characteristics of living things, allowing them to group objects as living, once alive and never alive. ● identify the food and living requirements of a variety of animals. ● identify imbalance in a meal and types of food that are less healthy when used extensively in a diet. ● identify types of human teeth by their shape. ● explain the need to look after teeth and describe how they should care for their teeth and gums. ● state that milk teeth are replaced by permanent adult teeth.	● show how groups share characteristics. ● understand the differences between herbivore, carnivore and omnivore. ● explain that individuals have different dietary needs based on health and the amount of exercise they take. ● use the term 'diet' correctly. ● identify examples of different categories of food and the ingredients of a balanced meal. ● describe the function of each type of tooth and link the types of teeth found in different animals to their diet. ● attribute tooth decay to bacteria.
Likely score on Test 3A	**0–2 marks**	**3–7 marks**	**8–10 marks**

Life Processes

Science Background

Living things carry out seven life processes, two of which are that they all feed and grow – so if an unidentified object feeds and grows, this is evidence to suggest it is alive. Sorting activities help the children to understand the difference between living and non-living.

Learning Objectives

Children should:
- know that things around us can be grouped into living and non-living.
- know that some non-living things were once alive.
- group objects and record groupings in tables or lists.
- use a Venn diagram to show how groups may share common characteristics.

Resources

- Collection of objects (or pictures of objects), both living and non-living
- A3 Venn diagram rings or hoops
- Pupil sheet A1

Introduction

Discuss the classification of living things with the children and challenge them with questions such as: *What makes a plant a living thing? Why isn't a wooden gate living if it came from a tree? Does a tree grow? Will the gate grow?* Discussion will give them reference points to make decisions when sorting the items you give them into sets. Ensure that the classification of problematic objects (for example, an apple, a leaf, a snail shell) are agreed by all the children.

Main Activity

Organise the children into groups. Before starting the activity, remind the class of the sets that they have decided on. Tell them to work as a group to decide which sets the items or pictures that you give them belong in. Explain that they may think some items belong in more than one set and that this is fine as long as they can explain their reasons. Allow the children time to sort their items, supporting them by use of open-ended questions. Most children will be able to sort by observation only. For those who need them, provide Venn diagram display frames or circles on A3 paper to sort physically. If some children want to sort objects into sets that share common characteristics, overlapping circles or Venn diagram frames might be useful – although the children may need to be shown how to use the intersection. Use pupil sheet A1 to record their results.

Plenary

Bring the children together and ask some groups to present their sets to the whole class. Agree what is good in the way different groups have presented their ideas. Some children may want to present their findings by physically regrouping objects in front of the class. Agree how to classify any objects that have presented difficulties for the children and record on the board that living organisms feed and grow.

What to Look For
The children should sort objects into groups according to specific criteria. Some children will be able to group accurately into living, once alive and never alive, and present their classifications clearly.

Living or What?

Name: _____ Date: _____

- Look closely at the pictures. Can you think of three groups that you can divide them into? Write the names of your groups here.

  _____

  _____

  _____

- Now sort the pictures into groups and record them using Venn diagrams.

- Did any fit into more than one group? Explain why.

  _____

  _____

  _____

  _____

- What did the items in your groups have in common?

  _____

  _____

  _____

- How do you know if something is living?

  _____

  _____

  _____

Your Challenge ...

- Think of ten things you might find in the garden and list them in three groups: **living**, **never living** and **once living**.

FOLENS SCIENCE IN ACTION: *Year 3* © Folens (copiable page)

A Square Meal

Science Background

Humans need a balanced mixture of foods to stay healthy. Carbohydrates (for example, potatoes, pasta, rice, bread and sugars) are energy-giving foods. Fats (such as butter and cooking oil) also provide energy. Protein foods (such as meat and fish) help us to grow and repair damage, and fresh fruit and vegetables help to prevent disease.

Learning Objectives

Children should:
- know that different animals need different conditions to survive and stay healthy.
- know that different animals eat different foods.
- know that an animal can be identified by its characteristics.
- know that humans need a balanced diet.
- know that a balanced meal contains starchy food, fats, food for growth and food for health.
- understand that foods in themselves are not unhealthy – it is always an issue of balance.
- know that some foods are healthier than others.

Resources

- Food (or fake food)
- Food diary
- Pupil sheet A2

Introduction

A topic about diet will be enjoyable if it is visually stimulating. Discuss the variety of foods different animals eat, names of groups and what animals need to stay healthy. Discussion will flow if examples of food or 'fake food' from a range of cultures are available. Encourage the children to talk about how people from different cultures may have different diets because not all foods grow everywhere. Ask each child to keep a food diary for a week before you carry out this activity. Introduce the idea of the food groups, giving examples for each. Children who are not ready for the correct names can use the terms 'food for energy', 'food for growth' and 'food for health'.

Main Activity

Organise the children into groups. Ask them to use one diary only and divide up one day's food into the main groups. Ask them to agree within the group the functions of the types of food in their samples. Encourage them to use terms such as 'these foods help us to grow'. When the groups have completed the task, bring them together and establish the function of any foods that have caused difficulties. Use pupil sheet A2 to record their findings.

Plenary

Ask the class to work on producing a suggested day's eating that would provide someone with a balance of the main food groups. It is important to emphasise that there are no 'unhealthy' foods but that there are some foods they should eat in small quantities only, and that they should have a balance of the main food types. As each item is suggested, identify which group it comes into and what it would allow the body to do. Be sensitive to individual differences between children during this topic. Children who are significantly over- or underweight often have low self-esteem. The purpose is to inform about healthy eating, not to judge. Pay attention to cultural and religious sensitivities.

What to Look For
The children should identify a meal that does not include all the components of a balanced diet and plan a balanced meal. They should identify types of food that are less healthy when used extensively in a diet, and identify examples of carbohydrates, fats, food for growth and food for health.

Food Diary

Name: _____ Date: _____

- Keep a diary of the food you eat each day for a week.
  Use that food diary to carry out the following tasks.

1. Choose one day from a diary of someone in your group.
   List the foods he or she ate that day.

   _____

   _____

2. Think what your body might do with each of the foods in your list.
   Record your answers in a table like the one below.

Provides Energy	Provides Energy Quickly	Repairs the Body	Helps Fight Disease

Foods can be divided into special groups called **proteins** (meat, eggs and fish), **carbohydrates** (potatoes, rice and sugar), **fats** (oils and butter) and fresh **fruit** and **vegetables**.

- Pick a new day from one of your group's diaries. Try to put the food eaten into the correct groups.

- Were any of the foods difficult to place? Why?

   _____

   _____

   _____

   _____

- From your food diary, choose a selection of foods to plan a healthy meal. Remember, it should contain a food from each of the groups above.

Your Challenge ...

- Plan a meal for someone who is in hospital. Remember to keep it balanced and tasty!

FOLENS SCIENCE IN ACTION: *Year 3*

Teeth

Science Background

In humans, digestion begins in the mouth. The teeth mechanically break up food: the chisel-shaped incisors at the front of the jaws cut food; canines, the pointed teeth, have a tearing action and are used by predatory carnivores to hold their prey; and, at the back of the mouth, flatter molars are used for chewing and grinding food. During chewing, the food becomes a ball impregnated with saliva, which makes it easier to swallow.

Learning Objectives

Children should:
- know that humans have three types of teeth.
- know that young children have temporary teeth called 'milk teeth'.
- understand that teeth have different shapes to enable them to do different things.
- know how animals' teeth are adapted to their diet.

Resources

- Model or poster of the mouth showing the teeth
- Small safety mirrors
- Reference materials (books and CD-ROMs)
- Pupil sheet A3

Introduction (1)

Some children will already have started to lose teeth and might be invited to bring in milk teeth to show the class. Show the class a model tooth (or the poster). *Which teeth have you lost? Can you show us where? Which shape of tooth was it? Did it look like this? This tooth is pointed, what do you think it does? Which animals have big pointed teeth like these?* Questions will allow the children to make generalisations from their knowledge. Introduce the different sets of human teeth. Explain that milk teeth need to be replaced because they do not grow and that small teeth in an adult jaw would not work effectively. Point out that permanent teeth will not be replaced and so they need to be cared for. Emphasise the need for regular cleaning to ensure that the teeth are clean and gums are healthy. A visit from the school nurse to talk about teeth and gums and how to look after them will reinforce the learning.

Activity (1)

Ask the children, in pairs, to examine each other's mouth with a mirror, using pupil sheet A3 to record what they discover. They should observe, identify and count the different types of teeth. Check safety precautions before allowing the children to examine each other's mouths. Use small plastic mirrors, sterilised in TCP and wiped dry with First Aid cotton wool. Advise the children not to put anything near their own or others' mouths.

Plenary (1)

Use the tooth model, or poster, to check the children's recall of the names of the different teeth and to summarise their function using scientific vocabulary. Explain that 'bite' means bringing two sets of teeth, not particular teeth, together, so words like 'cut' are better. Establish that 'chew' refers to the movement of the molars. Record the names of the teeth and the processes for the children (names are 'incisors', 'canines' and 'molars'; and processes are 'cutting', 'holding', 'grinding' and 'chewing').

What to Look For

Children identify types of teeth by their shape. They state that milk teeth are replaced by permanent adult teeth and explain the need to look after teeth because adult teeth are not replaced. They describe the function of each tooth. Some children link the types of teeth found in different animals to their diet.

 Do not use glass mirrors or dental mirrors. Children must not put the mirrors closer than a few centimetres from the mouth. They must not put any kind of probe into the mouth. The transfer of saliva can cause infection.

Teeth

Name: _____ Date: _____

● What do you think your teeth do?

_____

_____

_____

_____

_____

_____

Teeth are a very important part of the way we get our food.

canine

molar

incisor

● When did you first have teeth?

_____

● Will you have the teeth you've got now for life?

_____

● Use the mirror to look in your partner's mouth.
  Draw the different shaped teeth that you see.

● What job do you think these teeth do?

Teeth	What They Do
Canines	
Incisors	
Molars	

Your Challenge ...

● Do all animals have teeth? Find out if animals have certain types of teeth to suit the food that they eat.

Oh, I Wish I'd Looked After My Teeth!

Science Background

After eating, some food remains on the teeth. The mouth is an ideal habitat for growing micro-organisms, which use the food (especially sugar) to grow and reproduce. They form plaque, which irritates the gums and attacks the teeth. Thorough cleaning of teeth morning and night helps to reduce tooth decay and gum disease. Regular check-ups at the dentist prevent decay and disease from becoming too advanced for treatment.

Learning Objectives

Children should:

- know that teeth and gums are kept healthy by regular brushing with toothpaste.
- know that eating less sugar and regular visits to the dentist reduce the risk of tooth decay.
- know that teeth decay because plaque forms and encourages acid-producing bacteria.
- know that consuming less sugar helps to reduce plaque formation.
- raise questions that can be investigated.
- plan a fair test of an idea.

Resources

- Jars with screw tops
- Cola
- Sugar
- Vinegar
- A tooth (or use small, tooth-sized marble chips)
- Pupil sheet A4

Introduction (2)

Note: This lesson includes an investigation to be carried out over several days. A week before the lesson, put a marble chip (or a tooth if you have one) into fizzy cola and seal the jar with screw tops (see the safety warning at the foot of the page).

With the class, brainstorm ideas about tooth decay, establishing the causes and effects of tooth decay and gum disease. If you don't have real teeth available (which is likely!), explain to the children that the marble chips are being used because they are made of a similar material. Show the tooth in cola to the children during the lesson. Establish what has happened to the tooth and explain the causes. Challenge the children to come up with ideas about tooth decay that can be investigated. Prompt them to consider factors that may or may not be linked to decay, for example, they could investigate the effect of concentration of cola, sugar or vinegar on the rate at which the marble dissolved. Discuss how they could carry out a fair test. Ask the children to plan their test in small groups using pupil sheet A4.

Activity (2)

When the groups have planned their investigation, allow them to carry it out. They will need to leave the experiment for several days before they can see the results. The results will not be quantitative but it should be possible to conclude, for example, that marble dissolves in acid or cola (acidic) but not in water or sugar solution.

Plenary (2)

Encourage the children to discuss their methods and results. Ask what they did to make the test fair. Establish that acid dissolves marble. Explain that micro-organisms turn sugar into acid. Summarise and emphasise good practice in looking after teeth. Restate that they will soon be getting their permanent teeth. Explain why eating between meals can lead to tooth decay and establish that the children understand the importance of dental checks.

What to Look For

Children describe the connection between tooth decay and sugar and how they should care for their teeth and gums, including regular brushing and dental inspection. They suggest factors that might affect tooth decay and justify describing their investigation as a fair test. Some children attribute tooth decay to acid produced by bacteria and explain that reducing sugar intake reduces plaque formation.

 Sugar solutions and fizzy drinks stored in open containers at room temperature go mouldy. The children should use jars with screw tops. When marble is added to cola, gas pressure will build up in the sealed container.

Investigating Teeth

Name: _____   Date: _____

You are going to carry out an investigation about teeth.

- What do you want to find out?

  _____

  _____

- How are you going to do this?

  _____

  _____

- What must you do to make this a fair test?

  _____

  _____

- Record your results in the best way here.

- Now look at your results. Write down what you've found out.

  _____

  _____

Your Challenge ...

- Design a guide to healthy teeth.

Test 3A

Name: _____ Date: _____

1. Tick the correct box for each thing.

		alive	once alive	never alive
wooden stool		☐	☐	☐
metal spoon		☐	☐	☐

2. Link each box to a tooth. Then complete boxes i and ii.

| (i) Name: canine |
| Used for: |

| (ii) Name: molar |
| Used for: grinding food |

| (iii) Name: |
| Used for: cutting food. |

3. What do scientists mean by someone's **diet**? Tick the correct *answer*.

special food to lose weight ☐   *not eating very much* ☐

the food that they usually eat ☐   *a good balance of foods* ☐

4. Your diet can help keep your teeth healthy.

Write **two** more things that you should do to care for your teeth.

(i) _____

_____

(ii) _____

_____

Unit B

Helping Plants Grow Well

Scientific Enquiry: ● Scientists think creatively about how our world works and gather evidence to test their ideas using observation and measurement.	
Life Processes and Living Things: ● Living things all carry out seven life processes. ● Plants have life processes which are maintained by organs.	
Approximate Teaching Time: 12 hours	

Assessment Grid

Unit 3B

	Below level 2, children typically:	At level 2, children typically:	At level 3, children typically:
Green Plants	● identify parts of a flowering plant (for example, leaves, flower). ● know that plants need water to grow. ● know that plants produce seeds.	● distinguish between alive and never alive. ● justify saying that plants are alive with reference to their life processes and know that their growth is evidence of this. ● know that seeds grow into new plants. ● give examples of plant parts that are edible, such as leaves, seeds, fruits and roots. ● explain that water and light are needed for healthy growth. ● know that roots are essential for the plant's survival.	● distinguish between alive, never alive, and once alive. ● distinguish between movement from place to place and the ways in which plants respond to their environment. ● explain the function of the root and stem using scientific vocabulary. ● identify fruits as seed containers. ● recognise that too much water will prevent healthy growth. ● recognise that plants do not grow well if their leaves are removed. ● know that roots grow downwards and the shoot upwards, whichever way the seed is planted.
Likely score on Test 3B	**0–4 marks**	**5–7 marks**	**8–10 marks**

Plant 'Bits'

Science Background

Roots anchor a plant and absorb water and mineral nutrients. The stem transports these around a plant. In photosynthesis, water combines with carbon dioxide, which enters through the leaves, to form sugar (glucose) and oxygen. The energy comes from sunlight. Animals do not make new materials by photosynthesis. This is the distinction between plants and animals.

Learning Objectives

Children should:

- understand that plants are alive.
- know that the parts of green plants have names.
- know that roots absorb water and minerals and anchor a plant in the ground.
- understand that stems transport water (and nutrients) to all parts of a plant.
- recognise that the organs of green plants have specific functions.

Resources

- Drawings of some plants (daisy, dandelion, speedwell, buttercup)
- A variety of pot plants with two of the same variety
- Prepared bean seeds and fresh celery
- Food colouring
- Polaroid or digital camera
- An artificial plant
- Pupil sheet B1

Introduction

Ask the children to say what they know about plants and what more they would like to know. List these ideas. Then ask them to look at plants in the school field or in a grassed area that has not recently been mown. *How many plants can you see? Is grass a plant? Which plants can you name? What are the names of the parts of the plants?* Provide the children with drawings of the leaves of some plants. Challenge them to find these and to predict where certain plants will grow on mown grass. Back in the classroom, show the children some plants in pots. *What do all the plants have in common? What colour are all the leaves? How do we know that a plant is a living thing?*

Main Activity

Before the lesson, soak a bean seed for 24 hours and leave it to grow. Tell the children that they are going to keep plants in pots in school then ask them to complete pupil sheet B1, drawing the plant of their choice.

Show the children two plants of the same variety. Cut the roots from one of the plants and put it back into the soil. Explain that celery sticks are the stems of a plant. Encourage the children to look at the cut end of a stick of celery. *Where do you think the water and nutrients travel?* Place the bottom of the celery into coloured water. Photograph the celery and ask the children to predict how the celery will look in about ten minutes. Ask another child to take a picture after the colour has risen up the stem.

Plenary

Show the class both photographs and talk about what happened. At appropriate times, discuss what has happened to the plants with and without roots, and to the bean plant. Summarise that plants need water and certain mineral nutrients to remain healthy. The roots of a plant, as well as anchoring it, take in the water and minerals. These then travel through the stem to the other parts of the plant.

What to Look For

Children justify saying that plants are alive with reference to their life processes. They identify the parts of a plant and explain the function of the root and stem using scientific vocabulary.

Plants are Living Things

Name: _____   Date: _____

● What can a living plant do that a fake (or artificial) one can't?

_____

_____

● What do plants need to stay healthy?

_____

_____

● Draw a picture of a plant. Remember to look carefully at all the parts.
  Label the parts.

_____

● What colour are the leaves?   ● What colour are the roots of a plant?

_____   _____

● What will happen to a plant if the roots are cut off?

_____

● Look at the stem of the plant and touch it. What colour is it?

_____

● What do you think its job is?

_____

● Do you think it is strong? Why?

_____

Sowing the Seeds

Science Background

The life cycle of flowering plants begins with the germination of a seed, which develops roots and a stem system with leaves. Adult plants develop flowers, which contain the reproductive organs. The ovary grows into a seed container, which is called the fruit.

Learning Objectives

Children should:
- recognise that some plants have edible parts.
- identify common fruits and seeds.
- know that seeds have a role in the life cycle of the flowering plant.
- know that some familiar vegetables are fruits or seeds.

Resources

- Nuts (both in seed cases and without), apples, potatoes, carrots, seeds (mustard, runner bean, broad bean, sunflower and cress), avocados, oranges, capsicums (source of chilli and cayenne), bananas, coconuts
- Seed diary
- Cocktail sticks
- Reference materials (books and CD-ROMs)
- Pupil sheet B2

Introduction

Explain that we sometimes use plants, such as wheat and rye, to make flour. Show the children the nuts and explain that these are seeds that we eat. Cut open an apple to show the remains of the carpels, each with two seeds. Stress that fruits are the part of the plant that contain seeds. Cut open a potato and a carrot to demonstrate that they do not contain seeds. Use part 1 of pupil sheet B2 to reinforce the concept of a seed.

Main Activity

Present the children with the different seeds. Explain that they are going to try to grow some plants. The children should choose one variety of seed, soak them overnight and plant them in compost the following day. Ensure that they have labelled their pots clearly. Use part 2 of pupil sheet B2 to help the children record their observations as they grow. The children should then complete a seed diary, using the headings: 'Date seeds sown', 'Amount of water given daily', 'Date first shoots seen', 'Height after two days', 'Height after four days', 'Height after one week', 'Date second leaves appear' and 'Number of seeds that did not germinate'.

Stick three cocktail sticks into an avocado seed and balance it on a container of water. Germination will take several weeks but will provide a focus for further work.

Plenary

Present the children with the other fruits and ask them to predict what the insides will be like. Discuss what the purpose of fruits is. Discuss how their seeds have developed, including how the roots, stem and leaves appeared.

What to Look For
Children identify fruits as seed containers and know that seeds grow into new plants. They give examples of plant parts that are edible, such as leaves, seeds, fruits and roots. Some children recognise that fruits include bean pods, tomatoes and other examples that we often call vegetables.

 Children should always wash their hands after handling soil and should never ingest any seeds, fruit or vegetables in the classroom without the teacher's say so.

Fruits and Seeds

Name: _____ Date: _____

Part 1

- Write the names of as many fruits as you can.

_____

_____

_____

- Which of these fruits have seeds in them?

_____

_____

- What are seeds for?

_____

Part 2

You are going to grow some seeds and keep a diary about them.
- What do the seeds need to grow?

_____

- How long did it take for your seeds to start growing?

_____

- How many days was it before the plants had two sets of leaves?

_____

- Do you think that all seeds come from inside a fruit?

_____

- Where have you seen different seeds?

_____

Your Challenge ...

- Some vegetables, like potatoes, carrots and onions, don't have seeds inside them.
  Find out why this is and how these plants grow.

Plants Grow

Science Background

Living things grow. Some plants, such as grasses, grow quickly. Others, such as mature trees, grow more slowly. Growth is an increase in the mass of the plant: the height, girth, number of leaves and size of the root system all increase. The increase is the result of new materials being made by photosynthesis.

Learning Objectives

Children should:

- know that plants grow.
- know that growth is evidence that plants are alive.
- know that the leaves of a plant are important for growth.
- measure plant growth in a variety of ways.
- record results in bar charts.

Resources

- Four pot plants of the same variety and size (such as geraniums)
- Graph paper
- Balance
- Tape measures

- Clinometers (available from science and maths suppliers in a wide range of designs. The best models have either a trigger handle or a built-in viewer and enable readings to be calculated. Most versions come with notes on how to calculate a tree's height)
- Reference materials (books and CD-ROMs)
- Pupil sheet B3

Introduction

Visit the school field to show that plants grow in unexpected places. Point out that in summer grass has to be cut regularly and that some of the trees have new leaves. Ask the children to think about what changes as plants grow and which measurements would be the best indicator of how much a plant has grown. Back in the class, weigh and record the masses of four plants in pots and then strip most of the leaves from one and re-weigh it. Tell the children that they are going to observe the growth of the four plants kept under different conditions (one kept in the dark; one with no leaves; one with no water; one with everything). Discuss what they think will change. Elicit how the plants must be cared for before putting them in an agreed place. Give each child a piece of graph paper and explain that, in groups, they will record a different measurement (for example, height, thickness of stem, mass and length of leaves). They will then produce a bar chart with this measurement on the *y*-axis and the time (for example, days) on the *x*-axis.

Main Activity

With the children in pairs, ask them to plan which measurements to take and the duration of the investigation. (It will be easiest for groups to make measurements at different times.) Tell the children that it is their responsibility to collect measurements over the next few days. Use pupil sheet B3 to record the work. Talk about how trees grow and how their size can be measured. Suitable ideas include: estimate the number of leaves on a tree by roughly counting the number on one branch and multiplying by the approximate number of branches; or use a clinometer to calculate the height of a tree. Give the children opportunities to take measurements of trees.

Plenary

Discuss which methods of measurement give the best indications of growth. Follow up the work on graphs to show the growth of the two plants. Emphasise both the construction of the graphs and the outcomes. Use the results to conclude that plants are alive because they grow, and that the leaves are important for growth.

What to Look For

Children know that growth is evidence that plants are alive. They select and use a range of appropriate measuring devices and recognise that some methods of measurement are better than others. They represent numerical data in bar charts. Some children recognise that plants do not grow well if their leaves are removed.

Plant Investigation

Name: _____ Date: _____

You are going to plan an investigation to discover how plants change over time.

- What is the difference between the four plants you are investigating?

  _____

  _____

- What are you going to measure?

  _____

- What will you use to take these measurements?

  _____

- How will you record these measurements?

  _____

- How often should you measure?

  _____

- Record the measurements on the back of this sheet.

- Draw a bar chart on graph paper to show your results.
  Put the days along the bottom and the measurements up the side.

- What did you find out?

  _____

  _____

- How can you tell that these plants are living things?

  _____

Your Challenge ...

- Leaves are important for a plant to grow but not all plants have obvious leaves.
  Find out about cacti leaves and how cacti grow.

Plants Move

Science Background

Plant stems bend towards the Sun and leaves orientate towards the sunlight to ensure that the maximum amount of light falls on them. A plant grown in an area of restricted light will grow towards the light. Roots grow downwards and shoots up, irrespective of how a seed is planted. Plant roots will also grow in the direction of water.

Learning Objectives

Children should:
- know that plants are alive and that without roots they will die.
- know that plants move (turn or grow in particular directions).
- realise that animals move from place to place, but that flowering plants are anchored in the ground by their roots.

Resources

- The two plants in pots used in Lesson 1
- An artificial plant
- A video clip with time-lapse photography (e.g. of a field of sunflowers) to show plant movement
- A touch-sensitive plant, such as a Venus Flytrap
- A cardboard box
- Pupil sheet B4

Introduction

Establish that animals can move from place to place, and that different animals move in different ways because of their habitat. Encourage the children to observe that they can turn parts of their bodies without moving from place to place. Ask them whether they think plants move. Show the children the plant that has had its roots removed (from Lesson 1). Ask them to describe how it has changed when compared with the intact plant. Show a video clip with time-lapse photography to demonstrate the movement of leaves. Or ask about flowers opening and closing at different times of the day. Show them the artificial plant and establish that, unlike the living plant, it cannot respond to stimuli such as light and water. Show the children the touch-sensitive plant and ask why it reacts in that way.

Main Activity

Cut a small square in the side of the cardboard box and position the healthy pot plant inside it. Ask the children to predict what the plant will do. Allow the test to run for a few days and record the 'lean' of the plant. Turn the plant around and leave again. Allow the children to witness how the plant grows towards the light. You may need to repeat this a few times or even seal the box to convince them.

Plenary

Revisit the concepts of 'never alive', 'alive' and 'once alive' in relation to plants. Remind the children that one characteristic of all living things is that they move, and discuss the different ways that plants move. Use pupil sheet B4 to reinforce and assess the children's understanding.

What to Look For

Children distinguish between never alive, alive and once alive. They know that roots are essential for a plant's survival and they distinguish between movement from place to place and the ways in which plants respond to their environment. Some children know that roots will always grow downwards and the shoot upwards, whichever way the seed is planted.

Plant Movement

Name: _____ Date: _____

- Do animals move? _____

- What about plants? _____

- If plants don't get much light as they grow, what might a plant look like after a week? Draw your answer here.

- Some plants close their petals at night. Why?

  _____

  _____

- Other plants withdraw or shrivel up if you touch them. Why?

  _____

  _____

- Which parts can a plant move?

  _____

- An animal can move itself from place to place. Why can't a plant?

  _____

- What would happen to a plant with no roots?

  _____

- Moving is one of the things that tells us something is alive. Are plants alive?

  _____

Your Challenge ...

- Find out about other parts of plants and ways in which they can move. What would happen if you planted a seed upside down? Would the roots grow up and the shoots down?

Test 3B

Name: _____ Date: _____

1. (i) Draw a line to match each plant part to its name.
   (ii) Draw another line to match each plant part to what it does.

flower

carries water to all parts
of the plant

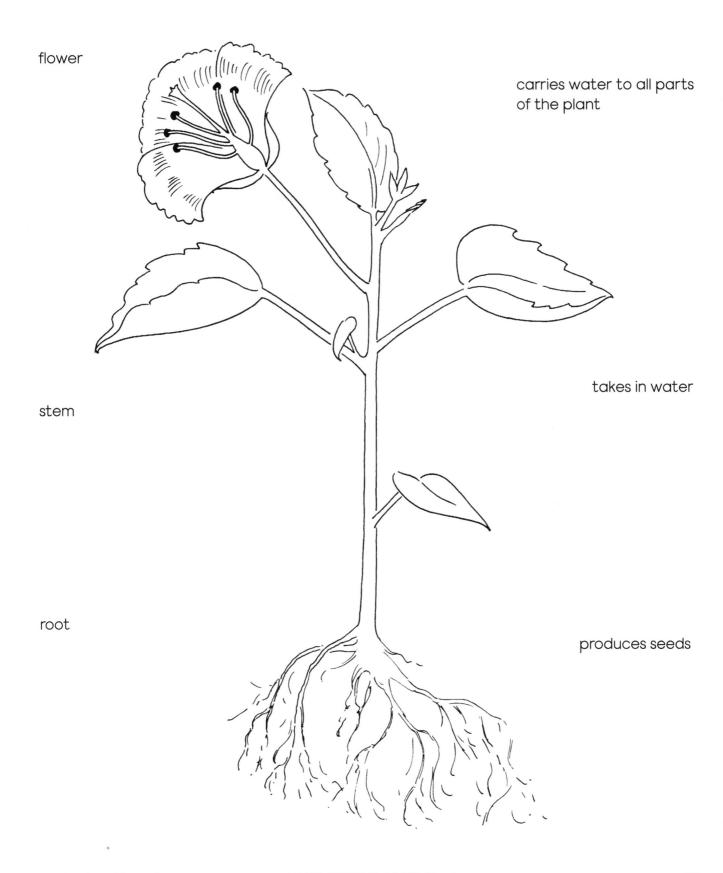

takes in water

stem

root

produces seeds

Test 3B (continued)

2. Which plant will probably grow best? Tick your answer.

A plant with lots of leaves and few roots. ☐

A plant with lots of leaves and lots of roots. ☐

A plant with few leaves and lots of roots. ☐

A plant with few leaves and few roots. ☐

3. It grows in part of a flower.

   People plant it.

   New plants grow from it.

   People pick it and eat it.

   It is a _____.

4. For healthy growth, plants need warmth, light and _____ .

5. Circle all of the following that are made from materials that were once part of a living thing.

   leather belt   granite steps

   paper bag   metal magnet   cotton shirt

Unit C

Characteristics of Materials

Scientific Enquiry:
- Scientists think creatively about how our world works and gather evidence to test their ideas using observation and measurement.

Materials and Their Properties:
- Different materials have characteristic properties.
- What we can do with materials depends on their properties and how they can be changed.

Approximate Teaching Time: 10 hours

Assessment Grid

	Below level 2, children typically:	At level 2, children typically:	At level 3, children typically:
Grouping and Classifying Materials	• describe the characteristics of materials and the changes they observe.	• say that materials are the stuff that things are made of. • describe materials in terms of their properties. • distinguish between natural and manufactured materials. • identify some materials as being of animal, vegetable or mineral origin. • give examples of uses for a range of materials.	• describe several properties of materials. • link property to function by identifying the property needed for a particular purpose. • differentiate between hardness and strength. • recognise that water goes through the holes in a fabric and that waterproofing blocks the holes. • know that elastic materials (normally) return to their original length when the weight is removed. • identify materials that take up most liquid as the most absorbent. • explain why absorbency is useful for certain jobs.
Likely score on Test 3C	**0–2 marks**	**3–7 marks**	**8–10 marks**

What Materials Are

Science Background

Material is the matter from which things are made. Materials are animal, vegetable or mineral in origin and can be classified as 'naturally occurring' or 'manufactured'. What we can do with materials depends on their properties and how they can be changed. We select materials by their characteristics. For example, glass is used for windows because it is strong and transparent.

Learning Objectives

Children should:

- know that materials are what things are made of.
- know that materials are animal, vegetable or mineral.
- know that some materials were once part of a living thing.
- know that materials have characteristic properties.
- know that some materials are natural, others are manufactured.

Resources

- Collection of tools in a black plastic bag (select tools which are made of only one material)
- Pupil sheet C1

Introduction

Ask the children to explain their understanding of the meaning of 'material'. Explore the concept of a material and build on this. It is important to ensure that they know that 'materials' are not limited to fabrics or clothes. Show the class a large black plastic bag containing tools. Ask the children what the bag is made of. Record the name of the material on the board, then play 'lucky dip' with individual children. Discuss what each tool is made of and why. Introduce the word 'material' and establish that materials are 'what things are made of'. Explain the use of the word 'fabric'.

Main Activity

Organise the children into groups. Ask them to record the name of each material that they can see in the classroom and where it is used using pupil sheet C1. Emphasise that they are thinking about the materials and not the objects. As the children work, prompt them to think about less obvious materials, such as brick, slate, aluminium and plants.

Plenary

List different materials in a table on the board. Begin to establish what constitutes a material by asking: *Can you see anything special about the things in the 'materials' column? What do these things have in common? Are any of them alive?* Encourage the children to identify the materials, to learn their names and to give an adjective, such as 'bendy', 'shiny', 'rough', 'smooth', 'clear', 'cold' and 'soft', which describes their properties.

What to Look For
Children say that materials are the stuff that things are made of and identify materials that are of animal, vegetable and mineral origin. They describe materials in terms of their properties. Some children distinguish between natural and manufactured materials.

Materials Around Us

Name: _____ Date: _____

 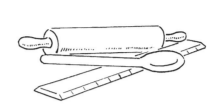 

● Look at the pictures. Write one word that would describe each set.

_____   _____   _____

● Write the names of any other materials that you can see in the classroom.
  Record your findings in the table.

Material	Things Made From the Material

● Write one material that came from an animal. _____

● Write one material that came from a plant. _____

● Write one material that came from a mineral. _____

● Look at the three pictures. What material has been used to make them?

Object	Material
window	
knife	
coat	

● Choose one material. Write why you think it has been chosen.

_____

Your Challenge ...

● Houses are built from lots of different materials. Make a table of the different materials
  that a newly-built house has. Make sure you put each material in the correct column.

Materials and Their Properties

Science Background

Properties are what makes one material different from another. The use of adjectives that have exact meanings, such as 'strong', 'hard', 'flexible', 'opaque' and 'transparent', allow us to describe materials accurately. All these adjectives describe how a material behaves under a certain type of testing.

Learning Objectives

Children should:

- know that adjectives allow us to describe materials.
- know that hardness and strength are not the same.
- explain why some tests might not be fair.
- plan and carry out a fair test.

Resources

- Different types of thread (including embroidery thread, wool and different thin cottons which break using a small force)
- Weights
- Graph paper
- Pupil sheet C2

Introduction

Ask the children to give examples of words that describe the properties of materials. Challenge them to name a material with each property and an object made from the material. For example:

Adjective	Material	Object
flexible	wood	ruler
strong	stone	bridge
transparent	glass	window pane

Then ask the children to work in pairs to produce opposites of the properties, and to identify a material with this property and an object that it could be used to make. Challenge them to write sentences such as 'Glass is hard but stone is strong' to distinguish differences in meaning of the terms. Use part 1 of pupil sheet C2 to assess their understanding.

Main Activity

Explain to the children that they are going to test different threads to find out which is the strongest. Show them an 'unfair' test, using different lengths of thread and different forces. Encourage them to identify the features of the test that are unfair, to give their reasons and to describe how they would set up a better test. Ask the children to touch the thread and describe what it feels like. *Does a material have to be hard to be strong?* Allow them time to plan and complete the test in groups, using part 2 of pupil sheet C2 to record their findings.

Plenary

Compare the findings from the groups and evaluate how successful the test was. Use some of the results to demonstrate how to construct a bar chart, with the type of thread on the x-axis and the mass needed to break it on the y-axis. Review the adjectives used to describe the properties of materials.

What to Look For

Children use appropriate adjectives to describe the properties of materials and differentiate between hardness and strength. They recognise an unfair test and, with help, plan and carry out an investigation. Some children plan and carry out a fair test independently.

 Do not use threads that require more than 500 g to break. Do not use nylon, catgut or similar strong threads. Children must wear eye protection. Make sure that children use lengths of thread that end no more than 10 cm above the floor.

FOLENS SCIENCE IN ACTION: *Year 3* © Folens

What is it Made From?

Name: _____ Date: _____

Part 1

● Draw a line to join the adjective to the correct material.

hard	cotton wool
transparent	metal
soft	plastic
strong	rubber
flexible	glass

● Can you name something that is strong and also hard?

_____

Part 2

Plan a fair test to compare the strength of different threads.

● Which **one** thing will you keep the same?

_____

● What will you change?

_____

● How will you make sure that the test is safe?

_____

● Describe your test.

_____

_____

● Record your results in this table.

Type of Thread	Weight Needed to Break it

● Which thread was the strongest? _____

● Draw a bar chart on graph paper to show your results. Put the type of thread along the bottom axis (x-axis). Put the weight it took to break it up the side axis (y-axis).

Your Challenge ...

● How could you make your test more reliable?

Stretching the Point

Science Background

A force applied to an object made of an elastic material will extend its length. When the force is removed, the object will return to its original length. Once a material has been stretched beyond its elastic limit, it is permanently distorted and will not return to its original shape. Inelastic materials such as perspex have a low elastic limit.

Learning Objectives

Children should:

- know that some materials are more elastic than others.
- know that elastic materials can be stretched but will return to their original length.
- turn questions into a form that can be investigated scientifically.
- use standard measures to quantify observations of length.
- use quantified results to draw conclusions.

Resources

- Elastic bands and elastic materials of various kinds (these could include different sorts of tights or elastic bandages)
- Weights
- Metre rulers
- Pupil sheet C3

Introduction

Write the word 'elastic' on the board. Establish that 'elastic' is an adjective and that it means 'stretchy'. Ask a volunteer to pull gently on the ends of an elastic band and describe what happens to the material – noting that it becomes longer when pulled and returns to its original length when released. *Are some materials more elastic than others?* Agree with the children that this is a question that can be answered with a scientific investigation, but point out that first they have to turn it into a form that will tell them what evidence to collect. *We need to know what we are going to do to the material and what we will observe as a result.* The children should realise that they will need to measure the sample before and after it has been stretched.

Main Activity

Ask the children to work through pupil sheet C3 to guide them in planning, setting up and conducting a fair test of elasticity. Use open-ended questions, as appropriate, to support the children and to challenge the more able.

Plenary

Show the children how to work out how much the materials stretched. Ensure that they understand that they need to subtract the 'before' length from the 'after' length to find the difference. Ask the children if all the materials stretched by the same amount; discuss any differences they found. They should understand that the greater the difference in measurements, the more the sample has stretched. Ask the class: *Do some materials stretch more than others?* Discuss their responses.

What to Look For

Children suggest how the original question can be turned into a form that can be investigated. They identify the observations and measurements that should be made and understand they use standard measures of length. They recognise that some materials are more elastic than others because they stretch more. Some children predict that the elastic materials will return to their original length when the weight is removed.

 Use only small weights and ensure that they cannot fall onto the children's feet. The children should wear eye protection.

How Elastic is it?

Name: _____   Date: _____

- Which of these materials is elastic?

  _____

- What does 'elastic' mean?

  _____

- Are some materials more elastic than others? Plan a fair test to decide which is the most elastic material out of the sample you have been given.

- How will you test the materials?

  _____

- What will you measure?

  _____

- Record your results in a table here:

- How will you work out which material stretched the furthest? Highlight the one that stretched the furthest.

  _____

- Which material stretched the most?

  _____

- What have you learned about elastic materials?

  _____

- Is there a way you can tell the difference between elastic materials and other types of materials? What do elastic materials do that others don't?

  _____

Your Challenge ...

- Do you think any parts of the human body are elastic? Give your reasons.

Soaking or Soak in?

Science Background

Some materials are waterproof – they do not allow water to pass through them. Materials were 'proofed' to prevent water penetrating them. Charles Macintosh, a Scottish industrialist, found that spreading rubber dissolved in naphtha onto cloth produced a waterproof fabric.

Learning Objectives

Children should:
- recognise that absorbent materials take up liquids.
- know why absorbency is useful for certain purposes.
- make decisions about the best method for an investigation.
- determine which measurements to make in order to gain the most useful results and what equipment to use.
- know that waterproof materials do not allow water through.
- know that some materials can be waterproofed.
- design a fair test and carry it out independently of the teacher.

Resources

- Jam jars and plastic containers
- Elastic bands
- Fabrics (some plastics and finely woven nylon and wool)
- Scissors
- Pipettes
- Water
- Wax crayons
- Water-based glue
- Blue food colouring (one drop in 200 cm³ water)
- Trays of water
- Different brands of paper kitchen towel
- Pupil sheet C4i
- Pupil sheet C4ii

Introduction

Begin by discussing with the whole class how we keep dry in the rain and which materials are useful. Describe what Macintosh discovered about spreading rubber onto cloth. *Was the cotton waterproof before Macintosh treated it? Was the rubber waterproof?* Provide the children with a demonstration. Use a square of thin cotton resting on a clear jam jar. Drop water on the fabric with a pipette to show how the water eventually travels through to the underneath. Explain that this is a model of what happens in real life. Discuss the children's ideas about which materials will hold water when it soaks it up.

Main Activity

Divide the class in half and explain the two investigations. The first challenge is to find out which material is the best for making cotton cloth waterproof. Use pupil sheet C4i as a prompt to help the children plan their test. Use questions to help the children to establish a method for preparing their own fabrics. *How will you add each one to the cotton? How will you add the materials to the cotton in a fair way? How will you add water to make a fair test?* The children need only add water in small volumes to carry out a fair test. It is useful to show the class how to place their treated cotton material on top of a clear plastic container, rather than glass jars or beakers. Demonstrate by pulling a piece of cotton taut over the plastic container and fixing it in place with elastic bands. Show how to place one of the sample materials on top of the dry cotton, pulling it taut and holding it in place with elastic bands.

With the second activity, it is tricky for the children to generate an accurate way of determining the absorbency of a paper towel. Begin by asking them how they would decide which towel is the best, and encouraging them to watch what happens when a few drops of water are placed on a towel. Three options are:

1. Use a tray full of (dyed) water. How many towels does it take to mop up all the water?
2. Drop 10 ml of water into the middle of the towel. Measure the diameter of the circle. The greatest diameter is the most absorbent towel.
3. Cut the towels into thin strips and hang them up (as from a washing line) with the tips in a tray of water. Measure how high the water has risen in a fixed time.

Hand out pupil sheet C4ii for the children to complete as they work.

Plenary

Allow each group to feed back their findings to others in class.

What to Look For

Children recognise that water goes through the holes in the fabric and that waterproofing blocks the holes. They describe how they tested the materials and justify saying that they carried out a fair test. Children identify which materials are the most absorbent and explain why absorbency is useful. They identify a method of testing the materials and how it may be kept fair. Some children justify their choice of method as giving more precise results.

How to Waterproof Fabric

Name: _____ Date: _____

You have been given a range of materials to help you to test which one makes cotton the most waterproof.

● Which one do you think will be best for waterproofing? _____

● Why?

_____

_____

● What are you going to do to test your materials?

_____

_____

● How will you make it a fair test?

_____

● Record your results here.

● Which material made the cotton the most waterproof?

_____

● Hold a piece of dry cotton up to the light. What do you see?

_____

● Try the same with the other pieces of material you have.
  Write your ideas about why some materials are waterproof on the back of this sheet.

Measuring Absorbency

Name: _____ Date: _____

Certain materials are used for jobs because of their properties (what they can do).

● Look at the picture. Why is the baby wearing the nappy smiling and the one in the paper bag crying?

_____

● What word do we use to describe materials that soak up water? _____

You are going to test paper towels to find out which is the most absorbent.

● Think of some ways you could do this and write them here.

_____

Choose the best method and describe what you will do.

● What will you measure? _____

● How will you measure it? _____

Record your results on the back of this sheet.

● Which towel was the most absorbent? _____

● Write the results in order, most absorbent first.

_____

● Was your test fair? _____

● How could you have improved your test?

_____

● Could you have tested the absorbency of the towels in a different way?

_____

Your Challenge ...

● Design a new nappy. Think about where materials need to be absorbent and where they need to be waterproof.

FOLENS SCIENCE IN ACTION: *Year 3*   © Folens (copiable page)

Characteristics of Materials

Science Background

It is the properties of materials that make them suitable for particular jobs. Sometimes there is a choice of suitable materials. For example, the materials used for building aeroplanes must be light enough for the plane to fly, but strong enough for the plane not to break up. Issues such as cost, durability, resistance to corrosion, weight and appearance must all be considered by technologists.

Learning Objectives

Children should:
- know that materials have a wide range of uses.
- know that all materials have several properties.
- know that the properties of a material determine what it is used for and that it is possible to justify why a material is chosen for a particular task.

Resources

- Clipboards (one between two children)
- Pupil sheet C5

Introduction

Talk about the materials that are used to make aeroplanes (the main structure is made of aluminium). Discuss:
- that the materials are chosen because of their properties
- that there may be more than one suitable material
- that technology can provide new materials that have more suitable properties.

Take the children outside and look at the materials used in the school building. Emphasise that each material has a specific property essential for its use (slates must be waterproof, bricks must be strong, glass must be transparent, and so on). Point out that there may be other properties that are important and that they need to identify these, too. (For example, flexible roof tiles would deform.) Encourage the children to pick out some common materials. It is important that they can distinguish between iron, copper, aluminium and brass (a mixture of copper and zinc) before finding them in school, otherwise they will always write 'metal'.

Main Activity

Provide pairs of children with pupil sheet C5 to survey the school (less able children need not try the *Your Challenge* section). They are going to identify the materials used for different purposes and decide why they were chosen. Encourage them to identify uses for at least six different materials (for example, glass because it is strong and transparent). Before sending the children out to do the survey, tell them to record the location of any material that they cannot identify. When they return to the classroom, organise them to record their findings in tables or quantitatively using bar or pie charts. Annotated diagrams of the school building, showing the names of parts, the materials used and their properties, can produce an interesting display.

Plenary

Discuss fitness for purpose. Remind the children that scientists and technologists are always interested in new and better materials, and that there is usually more than one material that can be used for a given purpose. If relevant to recent work, ask the children to compare the materials used for everyday objects in ancient times with those we use now.

What to Look For
Children accurately describe several properties of materials and give examples of uses for a range of materials, linking property to function.

Useful Materials

Name: _____ Date: _____

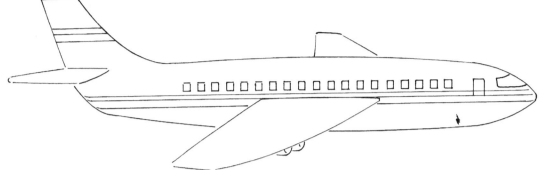

Materials are used for a purpose because they have the correct properties.

● You are designing a new aeroplane. What properties will the materials need to have?

_____

_____

● Now look at the different materials that are used around your school.
   Record them in a table like the one below.

Material	Where It Is	Why It Is Used

If you don't know what the material is, record where you saw it and find out later.

● Where did you find metals being used?

_____

● What makes glass a good material for windows?

_____

● What could you use instead of brick to build walls?

_____

● Do materials need to be attractive as well as have the right properties?

_____

Your Challenge ...

● You have been asked to design a container for a new drink. The company making the drink needs a cheap container that's easy to open and environmentally friendly. What material would you use? Draw the container and think about how you would decorate it to make it attractive to the buyer. Draw your design and think of a name for the drink.

FOLENS SCIENCE IN ACTION: *Year 3* © Folens (copiable page)

Test 3C

Name: _____ Date: _____

1. Tick which of the following best describes a material.

   any type of fabric   ☐

   the stuff from which something is made   ☐

   something made from non-living stuff   ☐

   something made from living things   ☐

2. (i) Circle **natural** or **manufactured** for each material.

   granite   ⟶   natural   manufactured

   wood   ⟶   natural   manufactured

   plastic   ⟶   natural   manufactured

   (ii) Circle **two** adjectives that best describe granite.

   elastic   flexible   hard   magnetic   strong   transparent

   (iii) Circle the correct word in this sentence.

   Granite is of **animal** / **vegetable** / **mineral** origin.

3. Marlon was testing different types of paper.

   He measured the width of the damp patch. The table shows his results.

Paper	Width of wet patch (cm)
A	3
B	2
C	5
D	4

   (i) Which paper is probably the **least** absorbent? _____

   (ii) Which paper would probably make the best towel for mopping up spilled water?

   _____

Test 3C (continued)

4. Jen hung weights from pieces of four different materials.

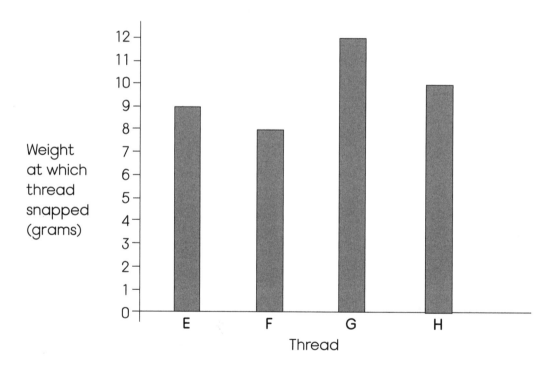

She measured how much longer each strip was with the weight on it.

Tick whether this is a test of:

hardness ☐   strength ☐   flexibility ☐   elasticity ☐

5. The bar chart below shows the weight needed to break a thread.

Weight at which thread snapped (grams)

Thread

(i) The threads are used to make ropes.
Which thread will probably make the strongest rope? _____

(ii) Which other property is important for material to make a rope? Tick your answer.

hardness ☐   flexibility ☐   transparency ☐   absorbency ☐

Unit D
Rocks and Soils

Scientific Enquiry: ● Scientists think creatively about how our world works and gather evidence to test their ideas using observation and measurement.	
Materials and Their Properties: ● Different materials have characteristic properties. ● What we can do with materials depends on their properties and how they can be changed.	
Approximate Teaching Time: 10 hours	

Assessment Grid

	Below level 2, children typically:	At level 2, children typically:	At level 3, children typically:
Grouping and Classifying Materials	● describe features (such as particle size) of different types of rocks and soils.	● recognise characteristics such as crystals, grains, layers and glassy appearance in rocks, and group rocks according to these characteristics. ● name some rock samples. ● describe features of a rock using a combination of everyday and scientific vocabulary. ● recognise the different components of soils. ● state that rocks are broken down to form a component of soil. ● recognise that larger-particle soils drain faster than smaller-particle ones.	● use the term 'permeable'. ● suggest uses for permeable and impermeable rocks and for hard and soft rocks. ● name the three types of rocks and know the connection between the physical appearance and rock type. ● name the different types of soil. ● predict that soils with the largest particle size will drain fastest and hold the most water. ● recognise that some soils are more suitable for growing plants than others, and that drainage is a factor. ● recognise the role of earthworms in adding air spaces to soil.
Likely score on Test 3D	**0–1 marks**	**2–6 marks**	**7–10 marks**

Differences in Rock Types

Science Background

Owing to the different ways in which each rock type was formed, there are observable differences between them. Igneous rocks, which formed underground, characteristically contain crystals. Volcanic igneous rocks (lava) may contain evidence of gas bubbles. Sedimentary rocks characteristically have a granular and/or layered appearance, and may contain fossils. Metamorphic rocks may contain layers of crystals or may appear glassy, or be deformed.

Learning Objectives

Children should:
- make increasingly detailed observations.
- group rocks by appearance.
- know that there are links between how something looks and how it was formed.
- know that there are three ways by which a rock may have formed.

Resources

- Collection of rock samples (a good selection would include: conglomerate, sandstone, limestone – sedimentary; slate, marble – metamorphic; granite and basalt – igneous)
- Reference materials (books and CD-ROMs)
- Pupil sheet D1

Introduction

Begin a group discussion with the class. Place a large collection of rocks on a table. Help the children to sort the rock samples into each of these categories: crystals, grains or layers.

Place a card sign with each pile. *What do all these have in common? They have crystals and they are quite hard.*

Main Activity

Divide the class into mixed-ability groups and give each group some rocks. Ask them to sort these rocks into three sets giving each set its correct name. When they have finished, ask the groups to record which characteristics the rocks in the sets share. Use part 1 of pupil sheet D1 to help them do this. Finally, ask them to write a riddle about one type of rock, using reference materials to help them, and record it in part 2 of the pupil sheet.

Plenary

Ask the children to try their riddles out on other groups before restating the three names for the types of rock. Play an interactive game by jumbling up sets of rocks and encouraging the children to regroup them against the clock. In classes with a wide range of ability, the games could take place in groups.

What to Look For

Children identify crystals, grains, layers and a glassy appearance in the rock samples they examine, and group rocks according to these characteristics. Some children name the three types of rocks and show evidence of the connection between the physical appearance and rock type.

Spot the Difference

Name: _____   Date: _____

The three different rock types were all formed in different ways. Because of this, they all have different characteristics.

Part 1

● Look at your rock collection.
  Divide the rocks into the three groups and record them in the table.

Has Crystals	Has Grains or Layers	Looks Glassy/Has Layers of Crystals

Each of these groups has a correct name:

Sedimentary rock has grains or layers.
Igneous rock has crystals or gas holes.
Metamorphic rock has a glassy look or has layers of crystals.

● Write the type of each rock at the top of each list in your table.

Part 2

Answer this riddle:

What am I?
I have a few crystals.
I am very hard.
I was made by a volcano.
What am I?

_____

● Now try to write a riddle of your own about one of the types of rock. Use books or other reference materials to help you, and you can make it as hard or as easy as you like.

Your Challenge ...

● Some rocks contain fossils. Find out which rocks they are and how the fossils got there.

Under Our Feet

Science Background

Soil contains both living and non-living materials. Some of the non-living materials, such as rocks and gravel, was never alive. Soil also contains dead plant and animal materials, as well as micro-organisms that help decomposition (decay) of this dead matter.

Learning Objectives

Children should:

■ compare different soils.
■ know that soil contains things that have died and things that have never lived.
■ know that there are different-sized particles in soil.
■ know the relationship between particle size, air space and the amount of water held by soil.

Resources

● The poem 'Under Ground' by James Reeves (if possible)
● Soil samples (natural or prepared from mixtures of soil, sand, clay and gravel – prepared by mixing a cup of compost, and half a cup each of gravel, sand, soil and clay)
● Tall (2 *l*) measuring cylinder

● 250 cm³ clear beakers (or jam jars)
● Small pebbles
● Gravel
● Sand
● Coloured water
● Hand lenses
● Pupil sheet D2

Introduction

If you have it available, the poem 'Under Ground' is a good introduction to talking about soil. *What things does the poet tell us are in the soil? Which of these things are living? Which have never been alive? What things might be found in soil that were alive but are not any longer?* Use a tall measuring cylinder and fill it one quarter full of the soil mixture described above. Top up the container with water, leaving around a quarter of the container to allow you to mix the soil and water together. Encourage the children to watch as the soil separates out. Discuss what they observe.

Main Activity

Each group will need three clear beakers one third full of small pebbles, gravel and sand respectively. They will need hand lenses to observe the samples. Use pupil sheet D2 to support their work. Ask the children to look closely at the samples and decide which sample would hold the most water and why. Then allow them to test their predictions about which sample will hold the most water using the material in the beakers. (Using coloured water helps the children to see when the air gaps in soils are full.)

Plenary

Establish what this experiment shows. Encourage the children to make connections between their observations – for example, that the larger the particles of soil, the bigger the air spaces. Show the children a piece of pumice. *Have any of you seen a pumice before? Where might someone have a pumice stone in their house? What is it used for? Does anything surprise you about the stone? Why do you think it is so light?* Encourage the children to observe that there are lots of holes in pumice and explain that this is why it is so light. Demonstrate this by weighing it. *Imagine that you dropped a pumice stone in the bath. What would happen to it? Why do you think this?* With the help of the children, demonstrate that the stone weighs more after it has been in water, even when it is towel-dried.

Why does this happen? (It has retained water in the holes.) Explain to the children the properties of a hard rock. Show them an example, scratch it along a softer rock and ask them to describe what happens.

What to Look For

Children recognise the different components of soils. They identify and record observations that compare different soil types (for example, in terms of particle size or air spaces). They also make connections between one characteristic and another such as 'the bigger particles have bigger air spaces between them'. Some children make further connections, such as predicting that soils with the largest particle size will also hold the most water because there is more space for the water to fill.

Looking at Soil

Name: _____   Date: _____

A ▭   B ▭   C ▭

- Look at and compare the three soil samples with a hand lens.
  Record the differences that you notice.

  _____

- You are going to add water to each beaker until it reaches the top of the sample.
  Which sample do you think will hold the most water?

  _____

- Why do you think that?

  _____

  _____

- Try out your prediction by adding coloured water.
  Measure how much water goes in each beaker.
  Record the amounts here.

Beaker 1	cm³
Beaker 2	cm³
Beaker 3	cm³

- Was your prediction correct?

  _____

- Why can that sample hold more water?

  _____

The soils around us are all different. Some are sandy, some are gravelly and some are based on clay.

- Which of these three soil types do you think holds the most water?

  _____

- Why do you think that?

  _____

  _____

Your Challenge ...

- Find out why few plants can grow on beaches and deserts.

Darwin and the Worms

Science Background

Some types of soil contain air gaps, and these gaps are useful when growing crops and garden plants as the soil will drain easily and allow enough water to penetrate down to the plant roots. There are many types of worm, one of which is the earthworm (*Lumbricus*). Charles Darwin postulated that, very slowly over time, as earthworms move through the earth, they turn over the soil, adding air to it. They also turn and mix the soil, passing out their worm casts and burying stones that were on the surface. This is why earthworms are useful to gardeners and farmers.

Learning Objectives

Children should:
- know that there are air gaps in soil.
- know that worms help plants to grow by providing air gaps.
- use investigation to draw conclusions.
- compare conclusions to those of famous scientists.

Resources

- Soil and clay samples
- Funnel and filter paper
- Wormery – a wormery can be made in a small aquarium tank. Remove the worms from some garden soil. Put alternate layers of soil (about 7 cm deep), chalk (3 cm deep) and sand (3 cm deep) in the tank. Put the worms in the tank. Add some leaves and leaf litter on the surface of the soil. Put black paper round the tank to keep it dark. The soil will need to be kept damp, but not allowed to get too wet, and take care to provide plant material (leaves, salad, fruit) on the soil surface as food
- Reference materials (books and CD-ROMs)
- Computer
- Water
- Pupil sheet D3

Introduction

Begin by talking about what soil is. From the last lesson, some of the children will remember the pieces of rock (sand and pebbles) and animal and plant remains. Show the children some clay soil, or some damp, malleable clay. Tell them that the particles in clay are so small that you cannot see the gaps, even with a hand lens. *What problems would this soil cause gardeners?* Demonstrate that clay soils do not drain easily by putting some clay onto filter paper in a funnel and pouring on water.

Main Activity

Establish that earthworms live in the soil and that, therefore, there must be air in the soil. Discuss with the children how they think air gets into the soil. Use part 1 of pupil sheet D3 to establish ideas about the usefulness of worms. Show the children how to make a wormery. *Why is it important to keep the sides of the wormery dark?* Ask the children to predict what will happen to the layers in the wormery over time. Leave the wormery for several weeks, observing the changes over time. Use part 2 of the pupil sheet to direct the children's observations and ideas.

Plenary

Towards the end of term, hold a class discussion about what has happened in the wormery.

What to Look For

Children recognise the role of earthworms in adding air spaces to soil and explain how investigations help us to explain what we see. They recognise the connection between their own findings and those of other scientists, such as Darwin.

The Wormery

Name: _____ Date: _____

Part 1

Both gardeners and farmers are pleased to have a large population of worms on their land.

● Why do you think this is?

_____

_____

Imagine a piece of stone on the top of the soil.

● What do you think might happen to it over the years?

_____

● Would you be surprised if the stone ended up a metre below the surface? _____
● How might it get there?

_____

Part 2

Observe your wormery over the next few weeks. Use what you see to help you with the following questions.

● What happened to the leaves at the top? _____

● Were the layers of chalk and sand mixed up? _____

● Were there any tunnels? _____

● What was in the tunnels? _____

● How would these tunnels help plants to grow?

_____

● A very famous scientist called Charles Darwin thought that stones were buried by earthworms. Do you think he was right?

_____

● How does your work with the wormery help to explain why Darwin was right?

_____

_____

Your Challenge ...

● Find out more about Darwin. Use books or the computer to help you.

Test 3D

Name: _____ Date: _____

1. Draw lines to match the three columns in the diagram.
   One has been started for you.

   silty soil   tiny particles   drains very slowly

   sandy soil   range of particle sizes   drains quickly

   clay soil   large particles   drains fairly quickly

2. (i) Describe what happens to water that falls on an impermeable surface.

   _____

   (ii) What is one way to make soil more permeable? Tick your answer.

   Get rid of as many worms as possible.   ☐

   Get rid of stones or large particles in the soil.   ☐

   Mix clay in with the soil.   ☐

   Mix gravel in with the soil.   ☐

3. Jack put a sample of soil in a container.
   He poured water into the container and shook it.

   (i) What type of material is most of the soil made of? Tick your answer.

   rock particles   ☐

   metal particles   ☐

   organic material   ☐

Test 3D (continued)

(ii) Which material in the soil floats to the top? Tick your answer.

small rock particles ☐

large rock particles ☐

metal particles ☐

organic material ☐

(iii) Jack wants to separate the soil into three different sizes of particle.
How could he do this?

_____

(iv) These are the different sizes of particle that Jack separated.

Each sample was up to the same level. He poured water into each container until it reached the same level in each.

Into which container did he pour the most water? Tick your answer.

The container with the smallest particles. ☐

The container with the middle-sized particles. ☐

The container with the largest particles. ☐

He poured the same amount into each. ☐

Explain your answer.

_____

_____

4. Which group of rocks often contains individual crystals? Circle your answer.

metamorphic   sedimentary   igneous

Unit E

Magnets and Springs

Scientific Enquiry: ● Scientists think creatively about how our world works and gather evidence to test their ideas using observation and measurement.	
Materials and Their Properties: ● Different materials have characteristic properties.	
Physical Processes: ● A force is a push or a pull. ● For any push/pull, there is a push/pull back.	
Approximate Teaching Time: 9 hours	

Assessment Grid

	Below level 2, children typically:	At level 2, children typically:	At level 3, children typically:
Forces and Motion	• describe how magnets pull on some materials.	• describe how magnets attract and repel one another. • compare the strength of different magnets. • identify materials that are or that are not magnetic. • identify how rubber bands change shape when pulled, that they pull when they are stretched and that they return to their original size when released.	• say that magnets do not need to touch to exert force. • use the terms such as 'pole', 'attract' and 'repel' correctly and generalise that like poles repel and unlike poles attract. • recognise that iron and steel are both magnetic and can be separated from aluminium by means of a magnet. • talk in terms of magnetic force going through materials or being blocked by materials. • use arrows to show the direction in which a force is acting. • use the term 'elastic' correctly. • predict that the greater the extension of the band, the greater the force and the further an object is propelled. • say that the force a spring exerts is in the opposite direction to the force you exert on it when the spring is compressed or extended.
Likely score on Test 3E	**0–2 marks**	**3–7 marks**	**8–10 marks**

Magnets

Science Background

Magnets are surrounded by a magnetic field. A field is a region around something that, under certain circumstances, can exert a force. A force is a push or a pull. Objects don't need to touch for the force to be experienced. Consequently, magnets can attract or repel each other without actually touching. Magnetic poles that are alike (for example, south and south) will repel each other if they come close. Unlike poles (that is, south and north) will be attracted.

Learning Objectives

Children should:

- know that magnets come in different shapes but they all have 'north' and 'south' poles.
- know that magnets can attract or repel each other.
- know that magnets do not need to touch to exert a force on each other.
- know that the 'north' pole of a magnet is the one that points North.
- know that like poles repel and unlike poles attract each other.

Resources

- Magnets (in as many shapes and sizes as possible – check they work before starting the activity)
- Home-made stick puppet
- Shoe box
- Clear bowl of water
- Cork (from a bottle)
- Needle
- Compasses
- Paperclips
- Pupil sheet E1

Introduction

Don't show the children the magnets straight away. Prepare a little 'magic trick' story (but don't let the children know that you are using magnets). Make a puppet with a magnetic base and stand it on the upturned shoe box (keeping it in place by holding a magnet under the box). Invent a short story about it, moving the puppet around on a journey by moving the magnet under the box, out of the children's view. At the end of the story, ask: *Is it magic?* and prompt the children to explain what they have seen.

Main Activity

The children need to gain experience of magnetic poles and attraction/repulsion. Identify the poles of the magnet for them. The convention is that the red end (or the marked end if the magnet is all one colour) is North-seeking. Encourage the children to explore magnets by placing identical poles close and then non-identical ones, and to record their results using the words 'attract' and 'repel'. Use pupil sheet E1 to support this.

Plenary

Before the discussion, collect a clear bowl of water (leave only a 2 cm gap below the rim), a disk cut from a cork, a magnetised needle and the compasses. Bring the children together and show them the compasses for finding direction. *Each of these contains a magnet. Where is it magnetic? Look what happens when I bring a magnet close. Now which bit do you think is magnetic?* Show the children that you have magnetised the needle (perhaps by picking up a couple of paperclips). Float it on the cork in the water and give the cork a gentle spin. *Does it point the same way as the compasses?* Explain that the Earth behaves like a magnet.

What to Look For

Children say that magnets do not need to touch to exert force and they describe how magnets attract and repel one another. They also use the terms 'pole', 'north pole', 'south pole', 'attract' and 'repel' correctly. Some children recognise that the north pole of a magnet points to the North and can generalise that like poles repel and unlike poles attract.

Magnets

Name: _____ Date: _____

You're going to investigate the properties of magnets. Use magnets to help you answer these questions:

● When you put a metal paperclip near the magnet, what happens?

_____

● Does the paperclip need to touch the magnet to be pulled towards it?

_____

● What happens when you put two magnets together?

_____

● Does it make any difference if you turn one magnet around?

_____

● We use the words 'attract' and 'repel' to describe the way a magnet behaves. Which word means push and which one means pull?

attract means _____ **repel** means _____

● Can you make a general rule about the ends (or poles) of the magnets? We call poles that are the same 'like poles'.

Like poles   _____

Unlike poles   _____

● A force is a push or a pull. Does a magnet make a force?

_____

Your Challenge ...

● The ends of a magnet are called the north and south poles.
Can you think of something larger that acts as a magnet and has north and south poles?

Magnetic Strength

Science Background

The most common materials attracted (pulled) by magnets are iron and steel (an alloy of iron). Cobalt and nickel are also attracted. Metals that are attracted to magnets are called magnetic materials. Alloys of these metals can also be magnetic. Some recent British coins are magnetic because they contain a steel core coated in non-magnetic copper. The strength of the pull of a magnet can be measured by making use of the magnetic properties of these metals.

Learning Objectives

Children should:

- know that magnets may have different strengths, even when they are the same shape.
- plan a fair test, deciding what to measure and how to measure it.
- record measurements.
- draw conclusions based on evidence collected.
- know that sometimes a magnetic force can pass through a material and sometimes the material shields it.

Resources

- Magnets (in as wide a variety of types and shapes as possible)
- Paperclips
- Sealed plate of iron filings (optional)
- Reference materials (books and CD-ROMs)
- Pupil sheet E2

Introduction

Show the children a selection of magnets during a circle time or a whole-class discussion. *Which magnet do you think is the strongest? Why do you think that? Where do you think the strongest bits of a magnet are? How could we tell where the strongest bits are?* Try holding paperclips on all parts of a bar magnet. If you have a sealed plate of iron filings, hold the magnet under the plate. The pattern of the filings will demonstrate that the poles have the greatest strength. Show the children how many paperclips you can hold on the end of a medium-strength bar magnet. Use part 1 of pupil sheet E2 to plan a test and predict the outcome.

Main Activity

Use part 2 of the pupil sheet to guide the investigation. Support the children by asking open-ended questions to prompt their thinking. Magnets can be numbered and, for less able children, the type of magnet can be included next to the number so that the children do not need to ask you to identify each one.

Plenary

What did you find out in your investigation? Which was the strongest magnet? Were the longest magnets always stronger? Encourage the children to realise that initial predictions may be based on non-scientific ideas – not all big things are stronger! Encourage them to explain in words what they have found out in their investigation. Choose two materials: one that allows magnetic force to pass through and one that does not. Show the children the effect and ask them why they think these differences occur.

What to Look For

Children compare the strength of different magnets and propose ideas for how to measure the strength of magnets in a fair way. They record results in tables and draw conclusions based on these.

Magnetic Strength

Name: _____ Date: _____

Part 1

You have a variety of magnets. You are going to test them to find out which is the strongest.

● How could you test them?

_____

_____

● What type of material do you need to help you with the test?

_____

● How will you make the test fair?

_____

_____

Before you start testing, record your ideas about the strength of the magnets in a suitable table on the back of this sheet. You will need to explain your ideas.

Part 2

● Now test your magnets and record the results below.

┌───┐
│   │
│   │
│   │
│   │
│   │
└───┘

● Were you surprised with your results? Why?

_____

● What have you learned about the strength of magnets?

_____

_____

● Are they stronger at certain points?

_____

Your Challenge ...

● Try to find out where magnets are used in everyday life. Use a CD-ROM or reference books to help you.

FOLENS SCIENCE IN ACTION: *Year 3*

The Recycling Plant

Science Background

Magnets are widely used in industry and in recycling. Often the magnets used in these places are electromagnets. When the current is disconnected, an electromagnet loses its magnetism, releasing whatever object it was holding. Most metals can be recycled, but it is not always viable to recycle iron and steel. In either case, these must be processed separately from aluminium. The differing magnetic properties of these materials makes a magnet an efficient means of sorting them since aluminium is not magnetic.

Learning Objectives

Children should:

■ know that not all metals are magnetic.
■ know that the common magnetic metals include iron and steel, and that aluminium is not magnetic.
■ know that recycling is important because it helps to save some of the Earth's natural resources.
■ understand that the whole community is responsible for the Earth's future, including children.

Resources

● Large copy of the recycling symbol drawn on paper
● Tray of objects (wooden lolly stick, plastic ruler, pencil, paperclip, aluminium disc, copper wire, iron nail and steel needle)

● Magnets
● Cans of various types
● Two posters promoting can recycling (if available)
● Large sheet of paper
● Pupil sheet E3

Introduction

Remind the children of earlier work on the properties of materials, when they found out that not all materials are magnetic. Show them the recycling symbol and ask if they know what it means and where they have seen it. Write the word 'recycling' on the board and discuss the significance of recycling.

Main Activity

Tell the children that knowing which materials are magnetic is useful when recycling them. Discuss the materials in a collection of objects that are like those they may have in their bins at home. Ask them to sort the collection into magnetic and non-magnetic materials. Then ask them to find the magnetic materials using a magnet, recording any unexpected outcomes. Use part 1 of pupil sheet E3 to support this work.

Plenary

Tell the children that recycling waste material can protect the Earth's resources. Make them aware that through promoting recycling they, too, can help to protect Earth's resources. Discuss how adverts use catchy slogans and other methods to interest people. If possible, show the children the two posters promoting can recycling and encourage them to consider which is better. Ask the children to use part 2 of the pupil sheet to design a recycling poster for steel and aluminium cans. Tell them that aluminium is easy to recycle and produces metal of high purity. Recycled aluminium needs only 5% of the energy required to make the metal from aluminium ore. Ask them to think about what information people need. How will they make their poster persuasive? They can then produce their poster on a clean sheet of paper.

What to Look For

Children identify metals that are and metals that are not magnetic, and recognise that iron and steel are both magnetic and can be separated from aluminium for recycling. They recognise the importance of recycling for the planet's resources and how they themselves can influence people's attitudes.

Recycling

Name: _____ Date: _____

Part 1

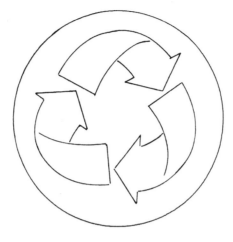

Some rubbish can be recycled. When doing so, it is important to separate magnetic materials from others.

● Predict which of your materials will go in each of these groups.
   Record the results in a table.

Magnetic	Non-magnetic

● Now use a magnet to check your list of magnetic materials.
   Do any of the materials you first chose not belong in that group?

_____

_____

● Check the other group.

Part 2

● People need to be encouraged to recycle materials. Design a poster to inform people about how to sort magnetic and non-magnetic materials. Make sure the poster is attractive and contains information to inform and persuade people to recycle. Make some notes on the back of this sheet, then draw your poster on some spare paper.

Your Challenge ...

● Find out about recycling in your local area. Do you recycle materials? Could you recycle more? Perhaps your school could start its own project.

Springs

Science Background

Springs are objects with elastic properties. Some springs can be extended and some compressed. Objects of elastic material will return to their original size and shape after having been stretched or compressed. However, there are limits to this beyond which they will not return to their original length. Hooke's law says that the extension of a spring is proportional to the load applied as long as the elastic limit of the spring is not exceeded.

Learning Objectives

Children should:
- know that springs can be compressed or extended.
- know that when springs are compressed inwards, they exert a force outwards.
- know that when springs are extended outwards, they exert a force inwards.
- know that the direction of a force can be shown by drawing arrows on a diagram.

Resources

- Variety of objects which contain springs of different shapes – items containing springs may include ballpoint pens (mattress, jumping suction toy, force meter, bathroom scales, kitchen scales, chest expander or a clockwork mouse)
- Pictures of objects which contain springs (such as motor cars or chairs)
- Large cut-out card arrows (some in blue, some in red)
- Pupil sheet E4

Introduction

You will need a range of items containing springs and a selection of compression and extension springs. *What do all these objects have in common? What makes them work? What happens to the springs inside them? Do different things happen to the different springs?* (The chest expander and force meter springs extend and do not compress, whereas the bathroom scales and mattress both compress.)

Check that the children understand the terms 'extend' and 'compress', then use pupil sheet E4 to consolidate the children's understanding.

Main Activity

Groups of children will need force meters and everyday items containing springs. The main purpose of this activity is to encourage the children to feel the forces exerted by springs and get used to the feel and direction of the forces before they actually measure those changes in their investigations over the next two lessons. Encourage them to consider, for each spring: *Does it extend, compress or both? When you extend a spring, what do you feel? When you compress a spring, what do you feel?*

Plenary

Show the children the red and blue arrows to demonstrate the extension or compression of some of the springs and the direction of the force. Encourage them to realise that the spring provides a force in the opposite direction to the force you exert on it. Ensure that all children experience this.

What to Look For
Children say that the force a spring exerts is in the opposite direction to the force you exert on it when the spring is compressed or extended. Some children use arrows correctly to show the direction in which forces are acting.

 Springs are dangerous. A spring stretched towards an eye is potentially blinding so children must wear eye protection. They must know appropriate safety rules for using the springs and must not extend them beyond their limit, nor put them near their eyes or the eyes of others.

Springs

Name: _____   Date: _____

  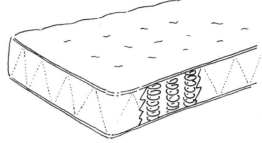

- What do all the items above have in common?

  _____

- What happens to a spring if you push it? _____

- What happens to a spring if you pull it? _____

- After you've pushed or pulled the spring, what does it do?

  _____

- Materials that return to their original size or shape after they have been pulled or pushed are called **elastic**. What other things can you think of that are elastic?

  _____

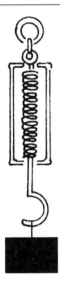

- Look carefully at the picture of the force meter. What do you think the spring is doing?

  _____

- What is making it do that?

  _____

- Which way is the spring being pulled?

  _____

We use the word **compressed** when an elastic material is pushed.
We use the word **extended** when the material is pulled.

- Look at the pictures at the top of the page. Write under each one if the spring can be extended or compressed.

Your Challenge ...

- When you compress a spring, you feel a push against you. Draw a red arrow on the pictures at the top of the page to show which direction the person is pushing or pulling the spring. Draw a blue arrow to show the direction the spring is pushing or pulling back.

FOLENS SCIENCE IN ACTION: *Year 3*

Stretching Patterns

Science Background

Like springs, elastic bands behave elastically. However, elastic bands only work properly in extension. A catapult consists of a length of elastic material that will store energy as it is pulled back. This will convert energy into movement as the object is propelled forwards.

Learning Objectives

Children should:

- know that elastic bands are elastic because they return to their original size and shape after stretching.
- know that the further back an elastic band is pulled, the greater the force it can deliver.
- know that the greater force an elastic band gives to an object, the further that object will travel.
- know that the heavier the object propelled by a catapult, the less distance that object will travel.

Resources

- Elastic bands
- Plastic tubs
- Weights
- Pupil sheet E5

Introduction

Make a simple catapult by attaching a piece of strong elastic to the legs of a stool or chair. Half pull the elastic band back and use it to propel a small paper ball across the classroom (away from the children). *What can you tell me about my catapult? What is it made of? What property does the elastic band have? What do we mean by elastic? How could I make my paper ball travel further?*

Main Activity

Catapults are best made from two long, thick elastic bands that have been knotted together at the centre. This will allow the band to be extended between the legs of a child's chair. If the bands are not long enough, add a third. This method allows the children to position their object accurately before release. Explain to the class that they will be carrying out two investigations and should use pupil sheet E5 to support their work. *How does the distance the elastic band is pulled back affect how far the object travels? How does the weight of the object affect how far it travels?* Before allowing the children to begin practical work:
- tell them the maximum extension for their catapult that will be safe
- show them how to mark the distance travelled by the tub
- check the children know where they should measure from and to.

Plenary

Discuss whether the children's predictions were confirmed and the reasons for them. Emphasise that the elastic bands pull back when they are extended and return to their original size when released (so they are elastic). Ensure the children understand that the greater the extension of the band, the greater the force it exerts on the object.

What to Look For

Children use the term 'elastic' correctly as an adjective and identify how elastic bands pull when they are stretched and return to their original size when released. They predict that the greater the extension of the band, the further the object is propelled, and express this in terms of greater forces. Some children predict that the heavier the object propelled by a catapult, the less distance that object will travel.

 Elastic bands are dangerous and potentially blinding so children must wear eye protection. They must know appropriate safety rules for using the elastic bands and must not extend them beyond their limit, nor put them near their eyes or the eyes of others.

Stretching Elastic Bands

Name: _____   Date: _____

You are going to investigate what happens to an object when it is fired from a catapult if you slowly increase the distance that you pull the elastic back.

- What distance should you start with?

  _____

- By how much will you increase the distance each time?

  _____

- What is the furthest distance you will stretch the elastic? _____

- What will you do to make the test fair?

  _____

- Carry out your test and record the results here.

Distance Elastic Stretched (cm)	Distance Tub Travelled (cm)

- What happened as you increased the stretch of the elastic? _____

- Can you explain why this happened? _____

  _____

Now carry out a second test to find out what happens to the distance an object travels when it becomes heavier.

- What will you need to keep the same each time you increase the weight?

  _____

- What will you change each time? _____

- Record your results here.

Weight of Object	Distance Travelled

- Look at your results. What happened to the distance the object travelled when the weight increased?

Your Challenge ...

- Can you explain why this happened?

Test 3E

Name: _____   Date: _____

1. Janine is pulling on the elastic band.

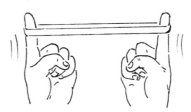

   (i)   Which way does the elastic band pull on each finger? Draw two arrows.

   (ii) Circle **True** or **False** for each sentence about the elastic band.

       It becomes longer when Janine pulls it.   **True**   **False**

       When Janine releases it, it returns to
       the length it was before she pulled it.   **True**   **False**

   (iii) Which property of rubber has Janine been exploring? Circle your answer.

             elasticity   flexibility   rigidity   softness

2. Sam tests four magnets by finding how many paperclips they hold.

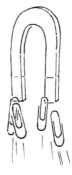

   (i)   Here are his results.

Magnet	Number of Paperclips in Chain
A	2
B	5
C	3
D	1

      Which magnet is the strongest? _____

   (ii) Will this investigation work with plastic paperclips? Explain your answer.

_____

_____

Test 3E (continued)

3. Iron is a magnetic material. This means that:

   two pieces of iron that are close together will pull together □

   two pieces of iron that are close together will push apart □

   a piece of iron will be pulled towards a magnet □

   a piece of iron will be pushed away from a magnet □

   Tick your answer.

4. Choose from the words in the box to complete the diagrams about magnets.

north	south	attracts	repels

   (i)

north pole	→ (attracts) →	_____ pole

   (ii)

south pole	→ (_____) →	south pole

5.

   Leo is pushing down on the toy.
   Draw an arrow to show the force from the spring on his hand.

6. Write the correct scientific term to finish this sentence:
   Stretching, pulling and squeezing are all ways of applying a _____ .

Unit F

Light and Shadows

Scientific Enquiry:
- Scientists think creatively about how our world works and gather evidence to test their ideas using observation and measurement.

Materials and Their Properties:
- Different materials have characteristic properties.
- What we can do with materials depends on their properties and how they can be changed.

Physical Processes:
- Light travels from a source.
- Light can pass through some materials but not others.

Approximate Teaching Time: 12 hours

Assessment Grid

	Below level 2, children typically:	At level 2, children typically:	At level 3, children typically:
Light and Sound	• describe reflective and non-reflective objects. • identify a number of different light sources.	• identify sources of light and explain what they have in common. • recognise that shiny objects are good reflectors. • describe the apparent movement of the Sun in the sky. • sort materials into those that do and those that do not let light pass through them. • explain that a shadow is formed when light shines on an object.	• say that non-shiny objects reflect light and that this is how we can see them. • sort opaque, transparent and translucent objects and materials correctly. • using scientific words, explain how a shadow is formed. • predict how shadows will change through the day. • predict that the size of a shadow changes as the object is moved in relation to the light source and screen. • recognise that the darkest shadows are made by opaque objects and bright lights. • recognise that the apparent movement of the Sun and the changes in shadows are due to the way the Earth spins on its axis.
Likely score on Test 3F	**0–1 marks**	**2–6 marks**	**7–10 marks**

What is Light?

Science Background

Light sources give out light and this travels from the source in a straight line. We see light when it enters our eyes. When light is blocked by an object, a shadow is formed. Materials and objects can be transparent, translucent or opaque.

Learning Objectives

Children should:

■ know that there are sources of light such as the Sun, flames and light bulbs.
■ know that we see objects when light from a source is reflected off the object.
■ know that shiny objects reflect more light.

Resources

● Dark place
● Torch
● Aluminium foil
● Resource Sheet 'What is Light?'
● Pupil sheet F1
● Reference materials (books and CD-ROMs)

Introduction

Take groups of children into a dark place, like a stockroom with no windows, and turn off the lights. *Why can't you see anything? What things could we use to help us to see in here? Can you think of things other than light bulbs? Would switching a TV on help*? Once all children in the class have had the opportunity to be in darkness and discuss light sources, review what they know and have suggested about light with the whole class. Introduce the term 'light source', using Resource Sheet 'What is Light?', and ask the children to complete part 1 of pupil sheet F1.

Main Activity

If we had a mirror in the dark stockroom, could we see it? Not if it was completely dark. Yet as soon as we switch one source of light on, we see everything. What must the things that we can now see be doing to the light? Encourage the children to recognise that these things must be bouncing the light back at you. Therefore, we see things because light is reflected by objects. Use part 2 of the pupil sheet.

Plenary

Review the phrase 'light source' and ask for examples. Ask how this helps us to see things. Review part 2 of the pupil sheet giving the list of things that reflect light and what they all have in common. Show the children the spot of light on a wall from a torch beam and demonstrate that it moves wherever the torch points. *Does the light travel straight or does it go round corners?* Emphasise that light travels in straight lines from its source.

What to Look For

Children identify sources of light and explain what they have in common. They recognise that shiny objects are good reflectors and say that even non-shiny objects reflect light and that this is how we can see them.

What is Light?

What is Light?

Name: _____ Date: _____

Part 1

- Cut out the pictures from the Resource Sheet. Sort them into two groups – one that gives light and one that doesn't.

- In terms of light, when are you unable to see things?

_____

- What do you need to be able to see them?

_____

- How do you think this makes it possible for you to see them?

_____

Part 2

Take a piece of foil and look carefully at both sides.

- What do you see?

_____

- Is there any difference in the sides?

_____

Now scrunch up the foil.

- What difference does that make?

_____

- Write a list of things that reflect light well and things that don't.

Reflects Light Well	Doesn't Reflect Light Well

- Do the things that reflect light well have anything in common?

_____

Your Challenge ...

- Find out about seeing the Moon. When we see it, it looks like a light source – but it isn't. How does it shine so brightly?

Blocking Out the Light

Science Background

Shadows are created when the light travelling in a straight line is blocked by an object. The shadow is the relative absence of light on the opposite side of the object from the light source. Shadows are never completely black because there is always some light reflected behind the object by other objects or from other sources.

Learning Objectives

Children should:
- know that the words 'transparent', 'translucent' and 'opaque' have very specific meanings.
- know that shadows are caused when the path of light is blocked.
- know that opaque objects produce the deepest shadows.

Resources

- Liquids in transparent glasses (for example, black coffee, water, clear apple juice, cloudy apple juice, orange juice, milk, tomato juice, soup and diluted blackcurrant cordial)
- Torch
- Pupil sheet F2

Introduction

Show the children the selection of liquids in transparent glasses. Then darken the room as much as possible. Shine the torch behind each of the glasses. *Which ones let all the light through? Which ones don't let any light through? Which ones let some light through?* All the solutions that are clear are transparent. It is essential that the children recognise that 'clear' and 'transparent' usually mean the same thing. Cloudy materials (frosted glass or milk) that let some light pass through but through which you cannot see an object distinctly are translucent. Materials through which no light travels are opaque.

Main Activity

Use pupil sheet F2 to explore the concept of shadow formation.

Plenary

Talk with the children about how shadows are formed. Encourage them to be accurate in their explanations. A key phrase to encourage is 'blocks out light'. Record the word 'block' on the board for them and explain that an object blocks light when light cannot travel through the object. Ask the children which sorts of materials block the most light. *Why do some objects make shadows that are not so dark?*

What to Look For
Children sort opaque, transparent and translucent objects and materials correctly and explain how a shadow is formed, using scientific words. They recognise that the darkest shadows are made by the combinations of opaque objects and bright lights.

Blocking Out the Light

Name: _____ Date: _____

Using a torch, work with a friend to make shadow puppets with your hands.

• What else could you use instead of your hands to make the puppet?

_____

• How does the material you use make the shadow?

_____

• What colour is the shadow? _____

• What do the edges of the shadow look like?

_____

• Why do you think they look like that?

_____

_____

• How could you make your shadow puppets as dark as possible?

_____

• Using what you know from the liquids you looked at in the lesson, can you explain why a piece of clear plastic wouldn't make a shadow?

_____

_____

_____

| clear glass | wood | card | glass from a bathroom window |
| water | metal | clear plastic | coloured plastic |

• Sort the materials above into three groups:

– Makes a good shadow _____

– Makes a shadow _____

– Doesn't make much shadow _____

Your Challenge ...

• People who use shadow puppets to put on plays can get facial features and detail on the clothing of their puppets. Use what you know about the shadows that different materials make to work out how.

Investigating Shadows

Science Background

Because light travels in straight lines, the size of a shadow depends on the distance between the light source and the object, and between the object and the surface onto which the shadow is projected – therefore, the closer the object to the light source, the larger the shadow.

Learning Objectives

Children should:

- know that the size of a shadow can be changed.
- carry out suitable measurements using simple measuring instruments.
- describe one change (such as torch to object distance) in relation to another change (such as height of shadow).

Resources

- Small torches and white paper for screens
- Lolly sticks
- Rulers
- Resource Sheet 'Investigating Shadows'
- Pupil sheet F3

Introduction

Remind the children about the previous lesson's work. Question them about how to make a shadow larger or smaller. Then ask them to predict how the shadows will change, and to explore the reasons for their ideas. If necessary, ask: *What will happen if you move the puppet nearer to the torch? What about further away from the torch?* Record the children's predictions. Tell them that they are going to find out how shadows change as the position of the object changes.

Main Activity

The children should use the puppet on the Resource Sheet 'Investigating Shadows' and pupil sheet F3 to guide planning and recording of the investigation.

Plenary

Establish the relationship between the variables. Children will have measured the distance of the object from the torch and the height of the shadow. Encourage them to use comparatives in their explanation (for example, 'the closer', 'the higher', and so on). Establish whether the children observed other things about the shadows by asking questions such as: *Were the shadows clear at the edges or were they fuzzy? Were the shadows the same shape as the puppet or were they different shapes?*

What to Look For

Children predict that the size of shadow changes as the object is moved in relation to the light source and screen. They use a ruler correctly to measure height and distance. Some children attempt a generalisation, such as 'the closer the puppet to the torch, the larger the shadow'.

Investigating Shadows

FOLENS SCIENCE IN ACTION: *Year 3*

Investigating Shadows

Name: _____ Date: _____

You are going to find out what happens to the size of a puppet's shadow when you change how far it is from a light source.

> **You will need:**
> - a torch
> - a lolly stick
> - a cut-out puppet from Resource Sheet 'Investigating Shadows'
> - a ruler
> - a screen

- Describe what you will do to find out what happens to the puppet's height.

  _____

  _____

- What will you need to do to keep the test fair?

  _____

- What measurements will you make?

  _____

- Mount your cut-out puppet on a lolly stick and try your test.

  Record your results here.

Distance from Torch to Puppet	Height of Shadow

- Did you notice anything else about the shadow as the height changed?

  _____

- Complete this sentence:

  As the distance to the puppet got bigger _____.

Your Challenge ...

- Try to explain why the height of the puppet changed using what you know about light travelling in straight lines.

FOLENS SCIENCE IN ACTION: *Year 3*

Sundials

Science Background

Owing to the spinning of the Earth, the Sun appears to follow a semicircle in the sky – it rises in the East and sets in the West. Because of the way shadows are formed and the apparent movement of the Sun, a shadow will move around a fixed object during the course of a day. As the Sun rises, the shadows of objects are long because the Sun is low in the sky. At midday, the Sun reaches its highest point (zenith) and the shadows are shortest.

Learning Objectives

Children should:
- know that the Sun appears to move in the sky.
- know that each day the Sun is lowest at sunrise and sunset and highest in the middle of the day.
- know that the higher the source of light (such as the Sun in the sky), the shorter the shadow.
- know that the Sun changes position in the sky becasue the Earth spins.

Resources

- Coloured chalk
- Compass points in the playground
- Reference materials (books and CD-ROMs)
- Pupil sheet F4

Introduction

Organise the children to observe and record the path of the Sun from the start to the end of school. Tell the children that they must never look directly at the Sun because doing so can damage their eyes. Use this as a resource for discussing the position of the Sun during the day. Encourage the children to say what they think would happen to shadows because of the change in the Sun's position by asking questions such as: *What will happen to the shadows at midday? What about in the early evening? Late evening?* Discuss the relationship between the compass points and the direction of the shadows.

Main Activity

Take the class into the playground and show them how to draw around their shadows, making sure they know the point at which they stood. Allow small groups of children to draw their own shadows. Repeat at hourly intervals. Use pupil sheet F4 to predict and record the investigation.

Plenary

Use the results from one group as the basis for a discussion about shadows. Establish what the children saw and how the shadows changed when the light was moved. Relate this to how shadows outdoors change throughout the day. Take the children outside and show them the compass point. Establish that the Sun rises (approximately) in the East and sets (approximately) in the West. Establish that when the Sun is at its highest point (zenith), it is in the South. Using the results of the investigation, ask the children to describe how shadows change in length from long in the morning to short at midday and long in the late afternoon. Explore the idea of using length/ position of the shadow to tell the time of day. Discuss time dials. Explore the idea about why we have apparent movement.

What to Look For

Children use their everyday experience and observations of the Sun to work out where to hold their torches to represent the Sun when changing the length of shadows. Some children generalise that the higher the light source (for example, the Sun or a torch), the shorter the shadow.

 Ensure the children never look directly at the Sun.

Sundials

Name: _____ Date: _____

You are going to investigate how the Sun appears to move in the sky.

- Look at the shadows your group has drawn in the playground. Draw them here.

```



```

- Use a colour to draw where you first marked your shadow.

- Then use a different colour to draw where you think the shadow will be in one hour's time. Continue to draw the position of the shadow each hour. Predict the position of the next shadow.

- Why do you think the shadow will be in the positions you have drawn?

_____

- Record the length of the shadows in this table.

Time	Length of Shadow

- Draw a bar chart to show the length of the shadow on a separate sheet of paper.

- What happens to the length of the shadow over the day?

_____

- When is it shortest? _____

- When is it longest? _____

- Why do you think the length changes?

_____

Your Challenge ...

- Until a few hundred years ago, people thought the Sun went round the Earth. Is this true? Find out who thought it wasn't. Why did it take a long time for people to believe this?

Test 3F

Name: _____   Date: _____

1. Circle each thing that is a light source.

    Sun   *button*   *street lamp*   *fire*   *mirror*

2. Circle the material that will make the darkest shadow.

    clear plastic   *cardboard*   *tissue paper*   *glass*

3. Draw a line to match each description to the type of material. You can draw more than one line for each description.

   This material lets through light, but you cannot see clearly through it.

   You can see clearly through this material.

   No light gets through this material.

   This material makes only a very faint shadow.

   transparent

   opaque

   translucent

4. Jake holds a torch so that it shines on a toy figure.

   Explain how the length of the figure's shadow will change as he raises the torch.

   _____

Test 3F (continued)

5. Complete this description of the way the Sun seems to move in the sky. Use the words from the box.

North	South	East	West

The Sun sets in the _____ . In the middle of the day, you can see it by facing

_____ .

6. This tree is in the Sun.

(i) At what time of day will its shadow be the shortest? Tick your answer.

in the middle of the morning ☐

about midday ☐

in the middle of the afternoon ☐

in the evening ☐

(ii) At midday, which way will the shadow point? Tick your answer.

North ☐   *East* ☐

South ☐   *West* ☐

7. Which types of objects reflect light? Tick your answer.

only shiny objects ☐

only matt objects ☐

matt and shiny objects ☐

only invisible objects ☐

Record Form

Name:

Area of Science	Level			Comments
Unit A: Teeth and Eating				
Scientific Enquiry	1	2	3	
Humans and Other Animals	1	2	3	
Unit B: Helping Plants Grow Well				
Scientific Enquiry	1	2	3	
Green Plants	1	2	3	
Unit C: Characteristics of Materials				
Scientific Enquiry	1	2	3	
Grouping and Classifying Materials	1	2	3	
Unit D: Rocks and Soils				
Scientific Enquiry	1	2	3	
Grouping and Classifying Materials	1	2	3	
Unit E: Magnets and Springs				
Scientific Enquiry	1	2	3	
Forces and Motion	1	2	3	
Unit F: Light and Shadows				
Scientific Enquiry	1	2	3	
Light and Sound	1	2	3	

Test Answers

Answers to Test 3B:

1.

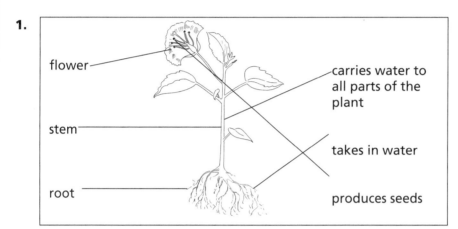

Names of parts correct *(maximum 3 marks)*   Functions of parts correct *(maximum 3 marks)*

2. A plant with lots of leaves and lots of roots. *(1 mark)*

3. Seed or fruit *(1 mark)*

4. Water (accept also plant food/fertiliser) *(1 mark)*

5. Leather belt, paper bag, cotton shirt *(1 mark in total)*

Answers to Test 3C:

1. The stuff from which something is made. *(1 mark)*

2. **(i)** granite/natural, wood/natural, plastic/manufactured *(1 mark)*
   (ii) hard and strong *(maximum 2 marks)*
   (iii) mineral *(1 mark)*

3. **(i)** B *(1 mark)*
   (ii) C *(1 mark)*

4. elasticity *(1 mark)*

5. **(i)** G *(1 mark)*
   (ii) flexibility *(1 mark)*

Test Answers

Answers to Test 3D:

1. silty soil ——— tiny particles ——— drains very slowly
sandy soil ——— range of particle sizes ——— drains quickly
clay soil ——— large particles ——— drains fairly quickly

(1 mark for each pair of columns correctly connected, maximum 2 marks)

2. (i) Credit answers indicating that the water does not soak in or drain away, for example, 'There will be lots of puddles', 'The water will collect on the surface', 'The surface will stay wet for a long time'.
Accept: It runs away. *(1 mark)*
(ii) Mix gravel in with the soil. *(1 mark)*

3. (i) rock particles *(1 mark)*
(ii) organic material *(1 mark)*
(iii) Use (two) different grades of sieve for the differently sized particles. *(1 mark)*
(iv) The container with the largest particles. *(1 mark)*
Credit explanations to the effect that this sample has the largest air spaces for the water to fill, for example, 'This one has the biggest holes so it holds the most water'. *(1 mark)*

4. igneous *(1 mark)*

Answers to Test 3E:

1. (i) Two arrows drawn parallel with the band pointing inwards from the two ends. *(1 mark)*
(ii) true, true *(1 mark)*
(iii) elasticity *(1 mark)*

2. (i) B *(1 mark)*
(ii) Credit answers explaining that the investigation will not work with plastic paperclips because plastic is not magnetic, for example, 'No, they will not be pulled by the magnet'. *(1 mark)*

3. a piece of iron will be pulled towards a magnet *(1 mark)*

4. (i) south *(1 mark)*
(ii) repels *(1 mark)*

5. Arrow drawn upwards. *(1 mark)*

6. force *(1 mark)*

Answers to Test 3F:

1. Sun, street lamp, fire *(1 mark)*

2. cardboard *(1 mark)*

3. Transparent – You can see clearly through this material **and** This material makes only a very faint shadow. *(1 mark)*
Opaque – No light gets through this material. *(1 mark)*
Translucent – This material lets through light, but you cannot see clearly through it. *(1 mark)*

4. It will get shorter. Do **not** accept: 'It will get smaller'. *(1 mark)*

5. West, South *(1 mark)*

6. (i) About midday *(1 mark)*
(ii) North *(1 mark)*

7. Matt and shiny objects *(1 mark)*